TIME-HONOURED KEEMUN

Tales of Tea about Chizhou

Under a wooden roof built over sixty years ago, the mottled iron sheet machine, as if out of control, sways amid the rumble. The concrete pillar stands by implacably, as if accustomed to the noise, while it holds the pulley that slowly moves the conveyor frame. The thick stain of tea seems to speak of the value of this living heritage.

在 60 多年前兴建的木质屋顶下，斑驳的铁皮机器如失去控制一般轰轰摇摆，混凝土柱子在一旁坚强地竖立，仿佛听惯了这嘈杂的"乐音"，随着皮带轮带动传送架缓缓运转，厚厚的茶渍仿佛在告诉人们这座活态遗产的价值。

TIME-HONOURED KEEMUN

Tales of Tea about Chizhou

Edited by the Editorial Board of
China Architectural Heritage

悠远的祁红——文化池州的「茶」故事

20C The 20th Century Architectural Heritage
Project of China: A Series of Books on Culture

UNICORN

Contents

目录

——

Preface One

序一

———

IT WAS AT THE RELEASE CONFERENCE OF the Second Group of China's 20th Century Architectural Heritage Projects held in Chizhou, Anhui Province, in December 2017 that I came to know about the old Keemun black tea factory in Chizhou. Today, seeing the sample copy of this book, *The Time-Honoured Keemun – Tales of Tea in Chizhou* which is going to press, I have to say I'm deeply impressed by three points: Firstly, the special significance of the discovery of Guorun Keemun factory by the expert team of the 20th Century Architectural Heritage Committee of China Cultural Relics Academy ; secondly, the great foresight and confidence shown by Chizou City in protecting and developing its cultural heritage; thirdly, Chizhou is not only home to 400,000 hard-working tea farmers, but more importantly, the land is brimming with confidence – as seen in Yin Tianji, a representative Guorun Keemun employee who is committed to defending the gold medal Keemun won in the 1915 Panama International Exposition.

Reading through *The Time-Honoured Keemun – Tales of Tea in Chizhou,* I find it has set a good example for spreading publicity about the first two groups of the 20th century architectural heritage projects, totalling 198, in China. That the old factory of Guorun Keemun dating back to the 1950s has been recognized as China's 20th century architectural heritage project proves how rare, unique and representative it is. The book tells tales that show Qimen of Anhui is the place of origin of the black tea of China and of the world at large. Valuing this heritage meets a historical and realistic need to promote Chinese tea culture. China's 20th century industrial architecture heritage is a treasure house of Chinese architecture; the old Guorun Keemun factory demonstrates not only the roots of this inheritance, but also how integrally creativity is related to cultural relics and museums, cultural tourism, industrial heritage, and history. A strong, guiding cultural policy from the government should be in place for its development.

I'm convinced that this book will be an important force in advancing the progress of Chizhou with regard to its cultural inheritance and creative design, and become a publicity guide for China's 20th century architectural heritage site of Guorun Keemun, and be an essential tome for promoting the cultural progress of Chizhou.

我是在 2017 年 12 月安徽池州召开的 "第二批中国 20 世纪建筑遗产项目发布会"上，知晓池州"祁门红茶"老厂房的情况。今天看到即将付梓的《悠远的祁红 —— 文化池州的"茶"故事》很感慨：一是中国文物学会 20 世纪建筑遗产委员会专家团队对"国润祁红"厂房的发现具有特别的意义；二是感慨池州市对文化遗产保护与发展的高度自觉与自信；三是在池州大地上不仅有 40 万辛勤耕种的茶农，更有守望 1915 年祁门红茶巴拿马万国博览会金质奖章的以殷天霁为代表的"国润祁红"企业员工的自豪感。

初读《悠远的祁红 — 文化池州的"茶"故事》一书，我明显感到有两个特点：其一，它为第一、二批中国 20 世纪建筑遗产的 198 个项目的传播带了好头。"国润祁红"20 世纪 50 年代的旧厂房入选"中国 20 世纪建筑遗产项目"，说明其遗产珍贵、价值独特，具有代表性。其二，该书用"讲故事"的方式，阐述安徽的祁门是中国乃至世界红茶的发源地之一。珍视这个遗产是做强中国茶文化门类的历史和现实需要。中国 20 世纪工业建筑遗产是中国建筑的宝库，"国润祁红"旧厂房展示的既是传承的基础，又是文博艺术、文化旅游、工业遗产、历史人文诸方面创意的融合，需要政府的主导和文化政策的导向。

我相信该书是在文化传承与创意设计方面推动池州建设的重要力量，成为认知中国 20 世纪建筑遗产"国润祁红"的宣传指南，成为文化池州建设的一个示范读本。

Shan Jixiang
单霁翔

President of China Cultural Relics Academy,
Director of the Palace Museum
中国文物学会会长
故宫博物院院长

August 2018
2018 年 8 月

Preface Two
序二

———

FROM THE DISCOVERY OF THE OLD GUORUN KEEMUN factory by the expert team of the 20th Century Architectural Heritage Committee of China Cultural Relics Academy, its inclusion on the list of the second batch of China's 20th century architectural heritage projects, to our discussion about it at Chizhou and the Hall of Embodied Treasures of the Palace Museum, the historical, technological, and cultural value of Guorun Keemun has grown increasingly obvious. The charm of Chizhou, in regards to both its landscape and its tea, is attributable to the slow tempo and the authenticity of life there, to the unique style of the Guorun Keemun factory, and to the Keemun people's commitment to the tradition. *The Time-Honoured Keemun – Tales of Tea in Chizhou* should be a guide for Chizhou to interpret the living culture of Keemun black tea.

As mayor of Chizhou Municipal People's Government, I keenly realize that on this land, with its long history, we have been home to numerous poets; we have Jiuhua Mountain Buddhist culture; the culture of scholarly officials about which the story of Crown Prince Zhaoming granting manors is well-known,; and

we have a rich ecology, reflected in the limpid water and lush mountains. But we have done far from enough in promoting Keemun and the heritage of the old Guichi tea factory, the birthplace of Keemun. As indicated by *Promoting Cultural Progress of Chizhou: The Research Report on the Creative Design of Anhui Guorun Tea Industrial Co., Ltd.*, Guorun Keemun has become a notable heritage site on account of the contemporary value of its industrial remains and cultural significance. Guorun Keemun is the most real, most vivid and most distinctive part of Chizhou culture. Still there today, Guorun Keemun is not only a treasure of Guichi Factory, but more importantly the public collection of Chizhou, reflecting the soul of the city.

I believe all readers of this book will come to love Keemun black tea, and will come to visit this culturally fertile city with its long history and rich tradition. The fame of Keemun and the cultural development of Chizhou will be mutually beneficial. I would like to express gratitude to the creative team behind *The Time-Honoured Keemun – Tales of Tea in Chizhou* for their contribution to the cultural progress of Chizhou.

自中国文物学会 20 世纪建筑遗产委员会
发现"国润祁红"老厂房，到它入选"第
二批中国 20 世纪建筑遗产名录"，再到
我们在池州及北京故宫宝蕴楼进行研讨，
"国润祁红"的历史科技与文化旅游价值
愈发凸显。我想，池州山水画卷乃至茶
韵之美，来自它节奏的慢、来自它生活
的真、来自"国润祁红"厂房的特有风格
与祁红人的文化坚守。今天《悠远的祁
红 — 文化池州的"茶"故事》一书摆在
面前，它应成为池州市向世人解读祁红
茶"活态"文化的指南。

身为池州市人民政府的市长，我愈发感
到，在这"千载诗人地"的沃土上有九华
山佛教文化、有昭明太子封邑的士大夫
文化、有好山好水的生态文化，而对于
祁红乃至孕育它的贵池茶厂老厂房的遗
产价值诠释得不足。从 2018 年元月中国
文物学会 20 世纪建筑遗产委员会等单位
编制的《文化池州建设 —— 安徽国润茶
业有限公司创意设计调研报告》中我看
到，"国润祁红"之所以应成为令国人瞩
目的"全遗产"，是因为它拥有一系列工
业遗存与文化遗产方面的当代价值。"国
润祁红"是池州应努力挖掘的最真实、最
生动、最具特色的文化"点"，它保留至今，
不仅是贵池厂的"宝"，更是池州市的"公
共收藏"，体现了城市的精魂。

我相信读者读过此书，会喜欢祁红茶，
会主动造访这清润怡人、悠远醇厚的传
统文化之城，祁红的盛名更会与池州的
文化发展之脉相契合。在此我感谢《悠
远的祁红 — 文化池州的"茶"故事》创
作团队为文化池州建设迈出的这一步。
特此为序。

Yong Chenghan
雍成瀚

Deputy Secretary of the CPC Anhui Chizhou
Municipal Committee and Mayor of Chizhou
Municipal People's Government
安徽池州市委副书记、市政府市长

August 2018
2018 年 8 月

Foreword   Keemun and Me

前言   历久弥新话祁红

UPON MY GRADUATION FROM THE
DEPARTMENT OF TEA Science, Anhui
Agriculture University, in 1986, I came to
work at the Guichi Tea Factory of Anhui
Province. As if in a twinkle of an eye, a good
32 years have passed by since then.

Back in the 1980s I was a young fellow,
and now I'm already middle- aged. Though
many things of the past have become a vague
memory, some things remain fresh in my
mind; the aroma of Keemun black tea in
the workshop where everyone worked to full
capacity; each production procedure; the
comparison and adjustment of tea samples,as
well as discussing them; the sight of the
old tea masters kindly making tea; and the
pleasure we had in our spare time, when my
fellow colleagues and I went to swim at the
spot where the Qiupu River joins the Yangtze.

Personal ups and downs are nothing. But
it is a great honor to witness the Guorun
Keemun Tea Business, to which I have
commited myself for a lifetime, and which has
stayed the course amid grand reforms, kept
sober-minded in prosperity, and never lost
heart or given up in adversity, finally achieving
a remarkable transformation and recognition.

We are always indebted to the older
generation for their all-out support for the
time-honoured tea business. For example,
Mr. Cheng Jiayu, Deputy Head (in charge
of techniques) of Guichi Tea Factory
of South Anhui Branch, CHINATEA,
worked as the technician at the Keemun
tea improvement site from 1939 to 1948.
While the factory enjoyed great prosperity,
the factory head Tang Kezhong never forgot
to develop new products and sent me to
Anqing Normal University to develop a
carbonated Keemun drink, which was a
very forward-thinking move.

I once left the factory to engage in tea
management. But when Keemun factory
found itself in difficulties, I returned back,
determined to work for it. At that time there
was nobody who remembered that Keemun
was one of the top three high-aroma teas in
the world, let alone set any lofty goals about
it. But I'm related to tea by both training
and calling. I remember the Keemun aroma
wafting in the workshop, and how the workers
were committed to making standard semi-
made tea samples. I believe such a world-class
tea should have a status worthy of it.

Keemun always takes pride in exporting
high-end products, but the later in-fighting
amid foreign trade to some extent worsened
the damage to the business. The black tea

industry was stuck in dire straits, and many changes took place in the industry. In spite of the fact that some factories which used to produce Yunnan black tea as their flagship product came to produce Pu'er in the main, Guichi Tea Factory has remained committed to producing Keemun.

I still remember that at China International Tea Industry Conference held in Changsha in 2007, Runsi Keemun stood out as the only one of its kind among the numerous Pu'er and Tieguanyin products. Zhan Lidan, Chairman of Fujian Tea Association, held my hand and said, 'Keemun is still there. It is really hard for you.' Mr. Hu Ping was former Minister of Commerce in charge of tea business. On an inspection tour, he visited our company and tasted 10-plus varieties of tea; he gave the Runsi Keemun *Jiu Wu Zhi Zun* very high praise, tantamount to a tribute.

With devotion and innovation, we got Runsi Keemun onto the list of China's Top 10 World Expo Brand-name Teas at Expo 2010. Once again, Keemun black tea shined at the World Expo, 95 years on from Panama International Exposition in 1915, winning glory for Anhui tea and inspiring the people people of Keemun. For this we received a congratulatory telegram from the Steering Committee of Anhui Province Agricultural Industrialization. On behalf of Anhui tea business community, we attended the global promotion program for Anhui, organized by the Ministry of Foreign Affairs of China in 2017. This caused some consternation. To address this, the organizer stated 'As the quality is ensured, please rest reassured'. And the Foreign Minister Wang Yi acclaimed Keemun as the noblest 'queen'. We always inject positive energy to the Keemun industry.

Soon after Yong Chenghan took office as Mayor of Chizhou, he accompanied Li Ke, Chairman of the Chinese Photographers' Association, on a visit to our company. The mayor was the first to point out that the Old Guichi Tea Factory should retain the cultural memory of Chizhou. After Wang Hong, Secretary of the CPC Chizhou Municipal Committee, made an inspection tour of the old factory, the experts like Xiu Long and Jin Lei also visited it, at the recommendation of Mayor Yong. Moreover, the old factory won the attention and favour of the highly accomplished cultural figure Shan Jixiang. Thanks to the celebrity's favourable comment, our flagship product the Runsi Keemun series has won a lot of praise from the industry, and the old factory has made it into the second list of China's 20th century architectural heritage. Guorun Tea is more than a business; more importantly, it has become a traditional and innovative culture that drives industrial development of the city.

The Japanese tea expert 山西贞 remarked that the Keemun aroma is a mixture of the aroma of rose and that of wood. It is an elegant smell, of years in the forest or the pleasant atmosphere of an ancient tea warehouse.

This book, *The Time-Honoured Keemun – Tales of Tea in Chizhou* has tnow been released. I would like to take this opportunity to express, on behalf of my company, gratitude to the team behind the book. We shall never let you down, as we will as always cherish our cultural tradition and continue to pursue innovation.

自 1986 年我于安徽农学院茶叶系毕业并任职安徽省贵池茶厂至今，不知不觉中 32 年过去了，正所谓"弹指一挥间"。

光阴荏苒，我这位 20 世纪 80 年代的新一辈已步入中年，很多事已记忆模糊了，但车间里溢满的祁红茶香，满负荷的工作，生产过程中各个工序、工位上的取样对比、讨论、调整，老茶师们神色宽厚地

看茶做茶，乃至工余同事们结伴在秋浦河入长江口处中流击水，仍历历在目。

往事中个人沉浮事小，能亲历钟情一生的国润祁红茶业在大变革中把握时代脉搏，兴盛时保持清醒，遇到挫折之际不气馁、不放弃，终于迎来了稳健转身与健康发展，则是人一生的荣幸。

不可忘这家近百年茶号得到许多前辈的鼎力扶助。例如程家玉先生，中茶皖南分公司贵池茶厂时期的技术副厂长，1939 至 1948 年间在祁门茶业改良场任技师；而在生产异常繁荣的情况下，唐克忠厂长仍不忘开发新产品的尝试，临时抽我到安庆师范学院联合开发祁红含气饮料，这是产业上极有远见之举。

我也曾离开茶厂从事茶叶管理工作，但在祁红厂遇到困境的时候，我决定回厂效力。那个时候几乎没人记起祁红是世界三大高香茶之一了，更没有为此打造的崇高目标。但作为一个学茶事茶的人，我回味车间里的祁红茶香，记得配制毛茶标准样时茶人们的敬业。我坚信："这样的世界级好茶绝不能明珠暗投。"

祁红一直以出口高端市场为荣，但之后外贸的内耗竞争在一定程度上加剧了对

行业的损害。其间红茶行业困境连连，同行中变故很多，比如有主打滇红的厂子适时地改为主打普洱，而贵池茶厂一直都在坚守祁红。

记得 2007 年长沙的中国国际茶业大会，在一片普洱、铁观音的汪洋中只有润思祁红一面红旗。福建茶叶协会会长詹立啖先生握着我的手说："祁红还在的呀，你们真不容易。"胡平先生是主管过茶叶的商业部部长，他曾到我们公司审评，品了十来款茶，对我们那款"润思祁红·九五之尊"予以了致敬般的嘉许。

由于我们的坚守与创新，润思祁红入选了 2010 年"上海世博会中国世博十大名茶"，此为祁门红茶自 1915 年巴拿马博览会之后时隔 95 年再次闪耀世博会，为安徽茶赢得了荣誉，唤起了祁红的觉醒，安徽省农业产业化指导委员会专电祝贺。2017 年，我们代表徽茶参加外交部安徽全球推介活动。有人对此提出质疑，而主办方的回答则是：品质好，放心。于是就有了王毅部长的盛赞："祁红 — 镶着金边的女王"的佳话。我们永远为祁红行业赋予正能量。

雍成瀚市长上任后不久，陪同中国摄影家协会主席李舸先生到公司，他率先指出老贵池茶厂应是池州的文化记忆。王宏书记专程到老厂区考察关心，之后，修龙、金磊等专家也在雍市长推荐下光临造访，又由此得到了文化大家单霁翔院长的重视喜爱。正是这些文化名流的参与，我们的主产品润思祁红系列不仅得到了业界的如潮好评，更使我们的老厂区入选"第二批中国 20 世纪建筑名录"。至此，国润茶业不仅是一种产业，更成为能推动城市产业发展的既传统又创新的文化。

日本茶学专家山西贞说祁红香是玫瑰香和木香的混合香，那仿佛就是森林里优雅的岁月味道，抑或是百年茶仓的馨香。

今值《悠远的祁红 —— 文化池州的"茶"故事》一书出版，我代表本公司全体员工感谢此书编撰团队的辛勤劳作！同时，也不负各界厚望，继续前行在文化守望与创新之路上。

Yin Tianji
殷天霁

Chairman of the Board,
Anhui Guorun Tea Industrial Co., Ltd.
安徽国润茶业有限公司董事长

July 2018
2018 年 7 月

Introduction

Today, knowledge and information are at our fingertips. While trees are still growing, rivers are still flowing, and clouds are changing direction from time to time, people are increasingly wishing to enjoy the simplest pleasures in life. In this context, drinking tea has grown to be part of a good life, as it is able to soothe the heart and purify the soul. It is refreshing to enjoy rich and aromatic tea. This book will lead the readers into the world of Keemun, that remains little known. In the book they will come across high praise for the aromatic Keemun – the noblest 'queen' in Foreign Minister Wang Yi's eyes. It should be said that Chizhou is the place of origin of 'Guorun Keemun'; Keemun is gift from Nature. More than anything, we should discover something, and start the journey to learn about the history of this tea, and savor it.

绪篇

在知识与信息可轻易获取的今日，树仍在生长，河水依然在流淌，云朵不时变换走向，人们却越来越希望回归生命本真的快乐。饮茶之风愈发高雅体面，更成为对自身心灵净化的精神之需。当茶的清香与醇厚甘甜隽永时，沁润在心田的每一寸便空灵舒静。本书将引领读者走进或许还鲜为人知的祁红世界，因为在外交部王毅部长赞美的"镶着金边的女王"中，人们还能品读到"祁红特绝群芳最，清誉高香不二门"的诗篇。应该说，池州是"国润祁红"的产地，祁红是自然赋予的宝物，重要的是我们该有所发现且在这里开启一次感悟茶史、品美味红茶的历程。

Be it in urban or rural areas of Great Britain, a strait apart from the European continent, we always picture gatherings in old stately homes; ladies and gentlemen, talking eloquently, holding tea cups brimming with gorgeous black tea, from which the fruity fragrance wafts around, and the taste rich and wonderful …

In this way, the Keemun black tea sold far away in Europe has been enjoyed by the likes of Shakespeare, Austin, Shelley, Keats and more through the centuries.

As far as China's social life (a tradition lasting thousands of years) is concerned, it is well captured by the saying, 'the most essential seven necessities for a home are fuel, rice, oil, salt, soy sauce, vinegar and tea', which illustrates that tea is a necessity for Chinese people of all backgrounds, throughout the ages. It must be pointed out that tea is more than just a necessity; it is an important component of Chinese culture. Centering around planting, drinking and savouring tea, generation upon generation of scholars and poets depict the aroma and charm of tea, and present scenes of savouring tea in an engrossing way, which is closely associated the Chinese poetry. Tea occupies a significant position in many literary masterpieces. For example, the tea fight between Su Dongpo and Sima Guang which is recorded in the classic stories, and Miaoyu cooking tea in *A Dream of Red Mansions,* convey the indescribable charm of Oriental culture. Modern writer Lao She observed human nature in his first well-known drama *The Teahouse.* Tea is undoubtedly a symbol of Chinese culture as China is the state of ceremonies, the nation of poetry, the source of silk, the originator of porcelain, and the kingdom of tea.

For China, the Latin is Chine. The provenance of this Latin word is such that we can see that westerners viewed China as being the country of silk, of porcelain, and of tea.

No-one could have predicted that in the second half of the 19th century, tea, a necessity for common people and a symbol of a Chinese-style elegant life, was more than connected with the people's livelihood and cultural consumption; it was used

A Painting of Tea Party in the Hui Mountain
by Wen Huiming, Ming Dynasty.

《惠山茶会图》，明代文徵明绘，

A Painting of Tea Fight by
Zhao Mengfu, Yuan Dynasty.

《斗茶图》，元代赵孟頫绘。

as a pawn in the economic strategies of estern powers and
became vital to the survival of the Chinese nation. Back then
the western powers, previously trading amicably with China,
switched to a more aggressive and avaricious policy, taking
advantage of their military might. The Britishplanned to
profit from dumping cheap industrial products in China but
came to find China had a very low demand for cheap Western
industrial products, but the British had a growing demand
for Chinese tea year on year, which led to a huge trade deficit.

In the 17th century, Catherine of Braganza (1638 - 1705), the daughter of King Juan IV of Portugal and the princess of King Charles II of England, stayed in history as the messenger who brought black tea to England. In 2016, Portugal made a five-euro coin with her and black tea as elements.

17 世纪，葡萄牙国王胡安四世的女儿，英国国王查理二世的王妃凯瑟琳·布拉干萨（1638–1705）作为将红茶传至英国的使者而留名青史。2016 年，葡萄牙分别以她及红茶为元素制作了五欧元硬币。

Compared with Asians, the British's first regard for tea was not aesthetic, but material.

The newly-published *Green Gold: The Empire of Tea* by Alan Macfarlane, from the perspective of a British anthropologist living in Assam, a tea production area in India, reveals Britain takes tea as a luxury and a weapon for redemption by delving into the colonial rule of the British Empire.

This phenomenon had long since attracted the attention of Karl Marx, who lived in London and was contemplating the future of Western society. He repeatedly contributed to *New York Review Daily* between 1853 and 1857. In *Trade with China*, Marx pointed out that the fabrics produced with machines in Manchester of Britain had no market in China, for "the price of the fabrics produced by the most advanced factory in the world turns out to be no lower than that of the fabrics made by hand on the most primitive looms". In addition, Marx recorded in *Revolution in China and in Europe*, "The import of tea from China was no more than 16,167,331 pounds in 1793, but the figure soared to 50,714,657 in 1845, and 57,584,561 in 1846. The figure has now topped 60 million (in 1853)." Other statistics shows that, by 1878, Britain consumed more than 136 million pounds of tea; each month an average British family earning a middle-to-low income spent 10% of the total family income in buying tea.

It was due to the international trade being on suchan unequal footing that the self-proclaimed advanced and culturally-developed powers represented by Britain used very brutal means to reverse the trade deficit by dumping opium in China, which led to the outbreak of conflicts between the East and the West in economic, political, cultural, military and other fields.

In the 17th century, Catherine of Braganza (1638–1705), daughter of John IV, King of Portugal, wife of the British King Charles II, made a name in history for distributing black tea tinBritain. In 2016, Portugal made five-euro coins featuring her image and black tea.

In 1657 Garway's Coffee House at Exchange Alley in London was the first seller of tea.

1657年，位于伦敦交易所巷（Exchange Alley）最先售卖茶叶的加韦咖啡屋（Garway's Coffee House）。

Against such a historical backdrop, the Western powers like Britain, while conducting unfair trade like dumping opium, went all out to develop new tea production bases so as to shake off their reliance on China for tea. In China, the tea industry, like all other industries, embarked on self-renewal for over half a century after 1840. There is a lot to be said about Keemun black tea suring this period.

Among today's tea world, the Keemun black tea produced from Chizhou and Huizhou, as well as the surrounding areas, is supreme. With its outstanding quality and enchanting aroma, it enjoys considerable fame throughout the world. It is one of the three famous high aroma teas in the world, with the other two being Darjeeling black tea of India and Uva black tea of Sri Lanka. For more than a century, Keemun has been the favourite drink of the British royal family, with its fame spreading far and wide, and it is always praised to be the 'Queen of Black Tea', as indicated by a poem that expressest that Keemun is peerless in terms of fame and aroma.

Once an elderly man from the Society for the Study of Chinese Architecture said, "Drinking Yunnan black tea is to remember the years of war, while savouring Keemun shows an elegant taste." The producer of this supreme black tea has gone through an arduous journey of setting up the business, safeguarding the business, reaching a nadir, seeking self-renewal, and regaining glory, which is reflected in the provenance of the 'Guorun Keemun' brand tea mainly produced from Chizhou, Anhui Province.

Tea-drinking usually contributes to harmony. But for Lu Xun (1881–1936), while drinking tea, he could not help venting anger, which is far from enjoying the happiness of leisure time. If we ignore all the glory and honor Lu Xun enjoyed, we see he loved smoking, drinking and enjoying tea as many people do.

It is a blessing to obtain and to be able to enjoy good tea. To have this blessing, the prerequisite is to takee the time to savour the experience in the first plac, and then enjoy the special feeling that comes with practice in this regard.

Others drank tea and drank kindness, but Lu Xun (1881 - 1936) drank tea and drank anger to enjoy Qingfu also became ironic. If Lu Xun is stripped of the halo in everyone's eyes, he is still a person who likes smoking, drinking, and drinking tea.

There is good tea to drink, and it is a kind of blessing to drink good tea. However, to enjoy this blessing, you must first have time, and secondly, you must have a special feeling of practice.

— "Drinking Tea"

别人喝茶，喝出和气，但鲁迅（1881–1936）喝茶，喝出怒气，享清福也成了讽刺。若剥去所有人眼中的光环下的鲁迅，他还是一个有抽烟、喝酒、饮茶喜好的人。

有好茶喝，会喝好茶，是一种清福。不过要享这清福，首先必须有工夫，其次是练习出来的特别的感觉。

— 《喝茶》

Black tea from the East gradually replaced alcohol and became a new favourite on the dining table of the British royal family.

东方传来的红茶渐渐取代了酒精，成为英国皇奉督桌上的新时尚。

On April 29, 1938, the Southwest Associated University Hunan, Guizhou and Yunan Tour Group arrived in Kunming. On the next day, the head of the Southwest Associated University posed for a group photo with the whole tutor team of the tour group. L3 and L5 in Row 1 are respectively Jiang Menglin and Mei Yiqi, and L5 in Row 2 is Wen Yiduo.

1938 年 4 月 29 日，西南联大"湘黔滇旅行团"抵达昆明。次日，西南联大负责人与旅行团辅导团全体成员合影。一排左三为蒋梦麟，左五为梅贻琦，二排左五为闻一多。

Hu Shi, native to Huizhou, kept *Canghui Study Diary*
while studying in Shanghai, which recorded the trivialities
of reading, enjoying tea, wine and operas together with his
friends when he was young. He mentioned he loved Maofeng
of Mountain Huang, Keemun black tea and Taiping Houkui.
When writing to his kinsman Hu Jinren, Hu Shi said, "Most
men of letters are fond of drinking tea, which enables them
to have new inspirations in literary creation." It must have
been a consensus among the men of letters and dignitaries.
Xu Zhimo, Yu Dafu and Lin Yuda were in contact with Hu
Shi. In addition to the tea produced from his hometown
Huizhou, Hu Shi also loved Longjing tea of Hangzhou.
Cheng Yuxin was an outstanding
business in Shanghai. In the late
20th century, an internal publicity
manual dated 1929 of Cheng Yuxin
Tea Business was found, its pages
brittle with age. The manual carried the
Hu Shi's inscription "Wishing that Cheng
Yuxin Tea Business enjoys long-time
prosperity"; and its title page had
the brief comment on China's tea
by Sun Yat-sen.

Chinese Tea Leaf

Japanese Tea Leaf

Chinese
Tea Plant
and Flowers

Ceylon Tea Leaf

India Tea Leaf

Seeds

The Chinese tea and flowers painted by
the French painter Pierre-Joseph Redouté,
who made a special comparison between
the tea leaves from China and those from
Japan, Sri Lanka and India.

法国画家皮埃尔·约瑟夫·雷杜德
（Pierre-joseph Redouté）绘制的中
国茶及花朵图，他特别就中国茶叶及
日本、斯里兰卡、印度等地产的茶叶
的不同进行了对比。

远在与欧洲大陆尚隔一道海峡的英国，无论都市或乡间，每一处古老宅院似乎都保留着这样一番景象：一众绅士淑女高谈阔论，手中茶杯泛着红茶绚丽的汤色，飘扬着似花似果的芳香，而入口的回味更是醇厚隽永……一个多世纪前远销到欧洲的祁门红茶就是这样与莎士比亚、奥斯汀、雪莱、济慈等一道萦绕在人们的唇齿之间。

就我们自己民族沿袭数千年的社会生活而言，一则古老的民谚概括为"自古开门七件事，柴米油盐酱醋茶"，可知饮茶的确是中国各时代各阶层民众的生活必需品之一，帝王将相、士农工商、巫医百工、贩夫走卒……概莫能外。尤其值得注意的是，饮茶在中国不仅仅是生活之必需，更是一种文化生活的重要内容。种茶 — 饮茶 — 品茶，历代文人骚客每每将茶香、茶韵凝聚于笔墨毫端，时有精妙的品茶场景描绘，与中国式的诗情画意筋脉相连。诸多文学名著中，如"三言二拍"里写苏东坡与司马光斗茶、《红楼梦》里描绘妙玉烹茶的情景等，具有东方文化难以尽说的清雅韵味；近代作家老舍也在其话剧名作《茶馆》中尽写世间百态。茶叶无疑是我们民族文化意义上的象征物之一 —— 礼仪之邦、诗之国度、丝绸之源、瓷器之鼻祖、茶叶之王国……

"中国"一词在拉丁文中写作"Chine"，按这个读音推测其汉字词源，至今众说纷纭 —— 丝绸之国、瓷器之国、茶叶之国，不一而足。虽无定论，但丝绸、瓷器和茶叶这三项确实代表了西方人对中国的最初印象。

谁也不曾料到，在 19 世纪下半叶，茶叶作为中国本土芸芸众生之生活必需品和中国式清雅文化之象征，其盛其衰却已经不仅仅事关本国生计与文化消费，而是与西方列强的经济战略相关联，进而成为事关中华民族存亡的大事。那时候，西方列强正在由东西方正常的商业贸易转向以军事强权攫取在华经济利益，因为原本打算向中国倾销大量廉价工业产品以获利的英国人，却发现那时的中国对西方廉价工业品的需求量很有限，反倒是本国对中国茶叶的需求量却逐年攀升，由此造成了巨额贸易

徽州人胡适，在上海读书时所做的《藏晖室日记》，记录了他年轻时与朋友读书、喝茶、饮酒、看戏的琐事。他说他喜欢黄山毛峰、祁门红茶与太平猴魁等。

胡适给族亲胡近仁的信中说："文人学者多嗜饮茶，可助文思。"这无疑是中国文人学者、高僧大德们的一个共识。徐志摩、郁达夫、林语堂等，都与胡适有交集。胡适除喜欢家乡徽州茶，还喜欢杭州龙井。程裕新是上海了不起的商号，20 世纪末有人找到已发脆的 1929 年程裕新茶号编印的内部宣传册，胡适为其题有"恭祝程裕新茶号万岁"的字样，扉页还有孙中山先生对中国茶叶的简评。

逆差。与亚洲相比，英国人对茶的第一印象不是人文美学的，而是物质文化的表象。[英] 艾伦·麦克法兰新近出版的《绿色黄金：茶叶帝国》，借由一个生活在印度阿萨姆茶产区的英国人类学家之笔，通过剖析英帝国的殖民统治，为英国将茶作为"奢侈品"和"武器"而赎罪。

这一现象早就引起了客居伦敦、正在研究西方社会命运的马克思的关注，他于 1853–1857 年多次投书《纽约每日评论报》。马克思在《对华贸易》一文中提到这样的史实：英国曼彻斯特机械化生产的布匹在中国没有市场，"世界上最先进的工厂制出的布匹的价格竟不能比最原始的织机上用手工织成的更便宜"。与此同时，马克思在《中国革命和欧洲革命》一文中陈述了这样的现象："从中国输入的茶叶在 1793 年还不超过 16 167 331 磅，然而在 1845 年便达到了 50 714 657 磅，1846 年是 57 584 561 磅，现在（1853 年）已超过 6 000 万磅。"其他资料显示，英国至 1878 年的茶叶消费量超过了 1.36 亿磅，一个收入中下等的普通英国家庭，平均每月的茶叶消费金额约占家庭总收入的 10%。

正是这场不对等的国际商贸，令自命'先进''文明'的英国等列强采取很不文明的手段去扭转贸易逆差 ——

Green Gold: The Empire of Tea. The author Alan Macfarlane, a widow of a tea farmer and tea merchant, has touched on things unseen in ordinary research works. The book covers interesting matter about tea, tea trade, tea dissemination, and how tea affects the world's history evolution.

《绿色黄金：茶叶帝国》
Green Gold: The Empire of Tea
作者艾伦·麦克法兰 (Alan Macfarlane) 作为一位茶农兼茶商的遗孀，使得这本书具有一般研究著作所难以涉及之处。书中内容涵盖了关于茶叶以及茶叶贸易、茶叶传播和茶叶如何影响世界历史发展进程等有趣的内容。

对华倾销鸦片，并最终导致了东西方经济、政治、文化，直至军事等各个方面的全面冲突"。

就是在这样的历史背景下，英国等西方列强在施行倾销鸦片等不正当贸易行为的同时，也极力在中国境外寻求新的产茶基地以摆脱对中国茶叶的依赖，而中国茶业界则与其他行业一样，开始了一场历时一个半世纪以上的自我更新（1840 年至今），其中很值得大书特书的是祁门红茶。

在当今的茶业界，出产于安徽池州、徽州一带的祁门红茶堪称红茶中的极品，以其卓越的品质、迷人的香气，在国际上享有至高无上的声誉，与印度大吉岭红茶、斯里兰卡乌伐红茶并称为世界三大高香名茶。百余年来，祁红一直是英国王室的至爱饮品，其香名远播，每每被赞为"红茶皇后"，如诗人所言："祁红特绝群芳最，清誉高香不二门。"

Keemun black tea
being processed.

加工过程中的祁
门红茶。

Black tea served on the dining table.

红茶被摆上餐桌。

曾有中国营造学社耆老说："喝滇红是为了记住抗战岁
月，而品祁红则是对一种优雅文化的品味。"这个红茶
世界的"群芳最"，有着一段跌宕起伏的"创业 — 守业 —
低谷 — 自我更新 — 再辉煌"的艰难路途，集中表现在
以安徽池州为集中产地的"国润祁红"品牌中。

徽州人胡适，在上海读书时所做的《藏晖室日记》，记
录了他年轻时与朋友读书、喝茶、饮酒、看戏的琐事。
他说他喜欢黄山毛峰、祁门红茶与太平猴魁等。

Rich soup in the container.

浓郁的茶汤在容器中。

The woman in Han clothing is
making Keemun black tea.

身着汉服的女子在冲泡祁红茶。

胡适给族亲胡近仁的信中说："文人学者多嗜饮
茶，可助文思。"这无疑是中国文人学者、高僧
大德们的一个共识。徐志摩、郁达夫、林语堂等，
都与胡适有交集。胡适除喜欢家乡徽州茶，还喜
欢杭州龙井。程裕新是上海了不起的商号，20 世
纪末有人找到已发脆的 1929 年程裕新茶号编印的
内部宣传册，胡适为其题有"恭祝程裕新茶号万
岁"的字样，扉页还有孙中山先生对中国茶叶的
简评。

Chapter One

A Century-old Black Tea Plantation in A Thousand-year-old Place of Poets: An aged Guichi tea factory, a double heritage site

The hardest part of the conservation and restoration of cultural heritage is to recognize and keep heritage alive. "All World Heritage sites have more than one important story to tell about their history: the way they were constructed or destroyed, the people who lived there, the various activities there and the happenings … " says the UNESCO's Management Guidelines for World Cultural Heritage Sites. The discovery of the former building of the Guorun Keemun Factory, and its subsequent inscription on the second list of the 20th-century Architectural Heritage Sites of China, is because of its 'living' tea production and the high quality of the tea of Keemun. The old building, though not particularly of aesthetic prominence, has practical functions which lend it an unadorned beauty. The traditional process and the modern production line, which are still in use today, represent a rare, unaffected model of 'total heritage'. All architectural heritage narrates, silently, historical changes and people that appear in its stories.

篇一

千载诗人地　百年红茶园
——双重遗产之贵池老茶厂

相对于文化遗产的修复与保存，最为困难的是对遗产的认定及坚忍不拔的传承，并使之"活在当下"。联合国教科文组织的《世界文化遗产地管理指南》中说："每个世界遗产地都不止一个重要的故事来说明其历史：它们是如何被建造的或如何被破坏的，曾经生活在那里的人，曾经发生过的活动和事件……"国润祁红旧厂房的发现乃至逐步成为第二批中国 20 世纪建筑遗产项目，贵在它拥有真实感人的"活态"茶厂及品质祁红。老厂房虽不特意追求美学，但功能实用，具备了建筑本体的质朴之美。沿用至今的传统工艺与现代化生产线，形成了不需要雕琢堪称珍贵的"全遗产"样板。因为建筑遗产无形中都会诉说或歌唱，它颂扬守望着那些有故事的历史变迁与呵护者。

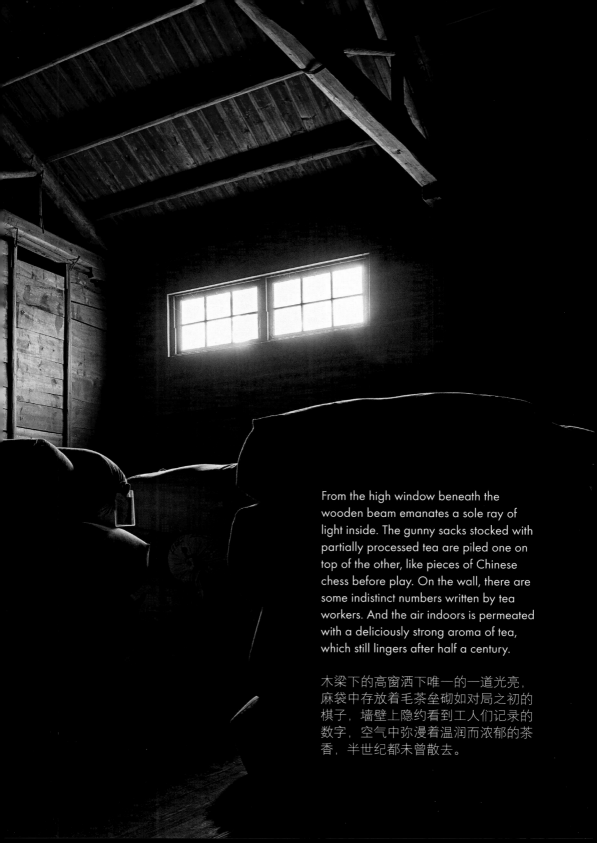

From the high window beneath the wooden beam emanates a sole ray of light inside. The gunny sacks stocked with partially processed tea are piled one on top of the other, like pieces of Chinese chess before play. On the wall, there are some indistinct numbers written by tea workers. And the air indoors is permeated with a deliciously strong aroma of tea, which still lingers after half a century.

木梁下的高窗洒下唯一的一道光亮，麻袋中存放着毛茶垒砌如对局之初的棋子，墙壁上隐约看到工人们记录的数字，空气中弥漫着温润而浓郁的茶香，半世纪都未曾散去。

CHIZHOU, ALSO KNOWN AS "QIUPU", IS A REFECTURE-level city in Anhui Province, located at the foot of Mount Jiuhua, on the south bank of the Yangtze River. With Guichi District, Dongzhi County, Shitai County, and Qingyang County under its jurisdiction, Chihzou borders Anqing City across the river to the north, Huangshan City to the south, and Jiujiang City, Jiangxi Province, to the southwest. It is an important part of the 'Two Mountains and One Lake' (Huangshan, Mount Jiuhua, and Taiping Lake) tourist area of Anhui; it is where Mount Jiuhua, one of the four sacred mountains of Chinese Buddhism, is located; and it is also one of the main port cities in the lower reaches of the Yangtze River.

Noted throughout the ages as 'a thousand-year-old place of poets', Chizhi is dotted with lots of sites of historic interest. It was officially set up as a prefecture nearly 1400 years ago, in 621 AD, the fourth year of the Wude era of the Tang dynasty. Back in the Southern and Northern dynasties, Chizhou was a fief granted to Xiao Tong (501–531), Crown Prince Zhaoming of the Liang dynasty, who directed the compilation here of

In Huizhou, where 70% of its land is mountainous, males usually left their homes early to make a living elsewhere as merchants, while females shouldered all the burden of picking tea leaves. Judging from the form of Huizhou tea, female tea farmers not only undertook the job of picking tea leaves, but they were also, hampered by the weather among other factors, responsible for the preliminary processing of tea. There is a vivid depiction of tea farming in a group of poems titled *Ballads on Picking Tea*.

"七山二水一分田"的徽州，男性早早便外出谋生，做着"徽骆驼"之工。采茶全由女性承担。从徽州茶叶的形态未考察，女性群体不仅承担了采茶工作，还受制于气候等限制。种植茶树的农家妇女还担负完成茶叶的初制加工。《采茶词》中有着如此形象描述。

問上松蘿第幾峰
小姑大婦同攜手
提籃出戶露方濃
曉起臨妝略整容
第二首

2.
By earliest dawn, I, at my toilet,
  only half-dress my hair,
And seizing my basket, pass the
  door, while yet the mist is thick:
The little maids and graver dames
  hand in hand winding along,
Ask me, "which steep of Sunglo
  do you climb today?"

縷縷旗槍起白毫
只圖焙得新茶好
且安貧苦莫辭勞
縱使愁腸似桔棒
第十九首

19.
But though my heaving bosom,
  like a well-sweep rise and fall,
Still patient in my poverty and care,
  I'll never shun my usual toil;
My only thought shall be to have
  our new tea well fired,
That the flag and awl be well
  rolled, and show their whiten'd
  down.

道是多晴卻少晴
西山日落東山雨
焙茶天色最難平
乍暖乍凉屢變更
第廿三首

23.
Awhile its warm, and then its cold,
  the weather's ever changing;
The sky is never so unsettled as
  when one wants to fire tea.
For as sun goes down the western
  hills, o'er the eastern hills
  there's rain.
Promising much fair weather, yet
  in truth but little comes.

插破儂家玉指尖
不知卻為誰甜苦
個中滋味兩般兼
茶品由來苦勝甜
第廿九首

29.
Among the kinds of teas, the
  bitter heretofore exceeds the
  sweet,
But among them all, both these
  tastes can alike bare be found;
We know not indeed for whom
  they may be sweet or bitter;
We've picked till the ends of our
  pearly fingers are quite marred.

the *Wen Xuan* (Selections of Refined Literature) – the earliest extant anthology of Chinese poetry and literature. In the Tang dynasty, poet Li Bai visited Mount Jiuhua thrice and toured Qupu five times; experiences which inspired his *Songs of Qiupu* among many other poems. The poet Du Mu once served as Governor of Chizhou, where he composed the *Qingming Festival*, a poem which made Apricot Blossom Village widely known. Such famous historical figures as Tao Yuanming, Su Shi, Yuefei, and Lu You spent part of their lives in Zhizhou, adding lustre to the place. Guichi Nuo opera, Qingyang qiang – the precursor of Peking opera, Dongzhi Lantern dance, among other cultural properties of Chizhou which have been made on the Chinese list of national intangible cultural heritage, were all quite popular in the city's history. Of the aforesaid tangible and intangible cultural heritage associated with the history of Chizhou, one thing was nevertheless more or less neglected, namely the fact that Chizhou has been one of the main places that grows and proceesses Keemun.

The Ceremony for Announcing the 2nd List of 20th-century Chinese Architectural Heritage, organized by the Chinese Society of Cultural Relics and the Architectural Society of China, was held in Chizhou, Anhui, on December 2, 2017, with Shan Qixiang, President of the Cultural Relics Society of China, Xiu Long, Chairman of the Architectural Society of China, among other experts, presenting architectural heritage certificates.

由中国文物学会、中国建筑学会主办的"第二批中国 20 世纪建筑遗产项目发布"仪式于 2017 年 12 月 2 日在安徽省池州市召开，中国文物学会会长单霁翔、中国建筑学会理事长修龙等业内专家为入选项目代表颁牌。

A scene of the 'Expert Review Session on Creative Designs with Respect to Industrial Heritage of Chizhou', jointly organized by the Chinese Society of Cultural Relics' Committee on 20th-century Architectural Heritage and the Municipal People's Government of Chizhou.

由中国文物学会 20 世纪建筑遗产委员会与池州市人民政府联合举办的"文化池州工业遗产创意设计项目专家论证研讨会"一角。

Participating experts talking about tea factory buildings.

与会专家介绍茶厂建筑状况。

But it is gratifying to see this oversight being remedied, step by step, since August 2017. On December 2, 2017, the 'Ceremony for Announcing the 2nd List of 20th-century Chinese Architectural Heritage and Inaugurating the Chizhou Academy of Eco-civilization', organized by the Chinese Society of Cultural Relics and the Architectural Society of China, was held in Chizhou, Anhui. Witnessed by about a hundred experts from the academia, including Shan Qixiang, President of the Cultural Relics Society of China, and Xiu Long, Chairman of the Architectural Society of China, the 66-year-old Guichi Tea Factory in Chizhou – the former Keemun factory building of Anhui Guorun Tea Industrial Co., Ltd. – was placed on the 2nd List of 20th-century Chinese Architectural Heritage. Before that, Anhui Guorun's Runsi Keemun processing techniques were included on the 5th Representative List of Provincial-level Intangible Cultural Heritage of Anhui.

At the northwest corner of the main urban area (formerly Guichi County) of Chizou today, on the south bank of the Yangtze River, is a factory complex characteristic of the early days of the People's Republic of China. From its location adjacent to the Chikou Wharf, it is not hard to speculate that this old factory probably shipped its products from the Chikou Wharf to the outside along the Yangtze River. Inside the factory, the building with its zigzag facade is typical of the Soviet-style industrial buildings of the 1950s. A short distance away from this building is a warehouse, the storerooms of which each have a wooden floor that adjoins the walls lined with wood panels; walking inside, one can smell a strong aroma of tea emanating from each piece of wood there. Now, this old factory has revealed its legendary past: A tea processing

Participating guests have a group photo taken in front of the Baoyun Building, also on the 2nd list of 20th century Chinese architectural heritage, in the Forbidden City.

与会嘉宾在同为"第二批 20 世纪建筑遗产"的故宫宝蕴楼前合影。

The entrance to the 66-year-old Guichi Tea Factory complex of Anhui Guorun Tea Industrial Co., Ltd.

拥有 66 年历史的安徽国润茶业有限公司的祁门红茶老厂房—贵池茶厂厂区入口。

factory named Guichi Tea Factory, built in 1950. Of a similar size in those days were the Qimen Tea Factory in Qimen County and the Dongzhi Tea Factory in Dongzhi County, both of which however disappeared as a result of drastic historical changes. More precious is the fact that the precursor of Guichi Tea Factory was a tea shop – where Keemun was invented by Yu Yuchen – on Yaodu Street, former Zhide County in Chizhou, about 70 kilometres away.

The former complex of Guichi Tea Factory, including the extant tea processing plant, the preliminarily processed tea warehouse, and the manual sorting plant among other things, was initially built in 1951. It was an exemplar of industrial architecture built in the early days of the People's Republic of China by applying building technologies from Europe and

Former Yaodu Street and the former Guichi Tea Factory.

尧渡老街及当年的红茶厂旧址。

Tea processing building with a zigzag facade.

剖面呈锯齿形的制茶厂房。

Soviet Russia among other places. A natural fusion of simple
appearance and functionality, the building complex represents
one of the few extant modern industrial complexes, and also
an objective record of the country's economic situations and
foreign trade policy – a shift to nationalization in agricultural
production. It has a strong air of modern industrial
architecture and a modern style of architectural art, but with
architectural functions designed to serve the processing of a
centuries-old farm product and several generations' aspirations
for a rich and strong nation.

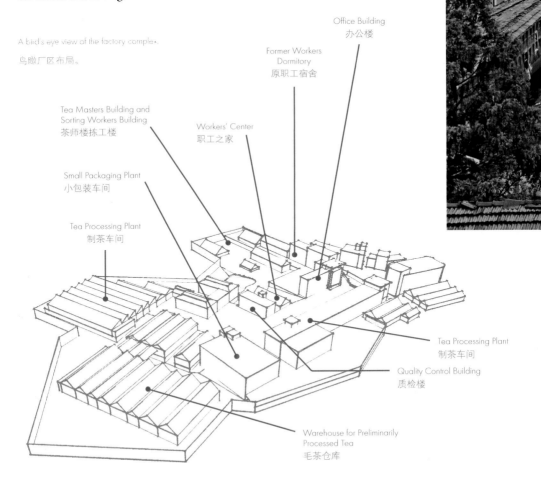

A bird's eye view of the factory complex.

鸟瞰厂区布局。

Office Building
办公楼

Former Workers
Dormitory
原职工宿舍

Tea Masters Building and
Sorting Workers Building
茶师楼拣工楼

Workers' Center
职工之家

Small Packaging Plant
小包装车间

Tea Processing Plant
制茶车间

Tea Processing Plant
制茶车间

Quality Control Building
质检楼

Warehouse for Preliminarily
Processed Tea
毛茶仓库

The tea processing plant with a
zigzag room, seen from the top
floor of the export warehouse.

自出口仓库顶层俯视制萃车
间，锯齿形的屋顶延绵不绝。

Tea Masters Building and
Sorting Workers Building.

茶师楼与拣工楼。

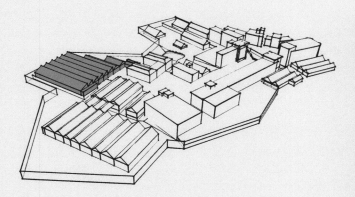

Tea Processing Plant
制茶车间

The tea-processing plant is the largest building inside the factory, whose roof is a combination of six mono-pitched roofs, with a zigzag facade. Inside is a network of colossal cement columns, without partitions. Each of the mono-pitched roofs is made up by a vertical glass wall and a tiled slope. The cement columns are hollow inside and were actually used as a drainage system. The machines inside, which were imported in 1950 with specially designed production functions, are still usable today. This plant guaranteed mass production of Keemun in the stages of 'refinement'. Architecturally, this building was evidently influenced by Soviet-style industrial architecture at the time, with a plain appearance favouring practical functions.

制茶车间是老厂区内占地面积最大的建筑，外观由六个一面坡屋顶并联组成大车间屋顶，立面呈锯齿状；室内由巨大的水泥柱形成无隔断墙的柱网空间。其一面坡顶为垂直的玻璃墙与斜坡之瓦面组成，水泥柱中空，实为排水管道。室内机械设备为 1950 年进口设备，其生产功能经专门设计，至今仍可使用。此车间保证了祁红生产"精制工艺"阶段的大规模生产量。就建筑本体而言，制茶车间明显受当年苏式工业建筑风格影响，外观简洁朴素，以保证实用功能为首要。

新 机 房

　　新机房1961年4月施工，1962年5月竣工。据老职工回忆当时有8个施工队同时施工，场面非常壮观。整体建筑规整，风格简约，较多地采用了新技术、新结构、新材料，代表了当时茶产业的最高水平。它的内部采用大跨度设计，以12根圆形廊柱为支撑。更为珍贵的是新机房内装备了当时国内最传统的祁门红茶联装生产流水线，这些制茶老设备得到了较好保护和适当使用。

New machinery room

The full name of the new machinery room is hand-picked field. Its history can be traced back to 1962.

The new machinery room was constructed from April 1961 to May 1962. The construction took 13 months. According to the elder workers' memory, the building was constructed by 8 teams at same time. The scene was very spectacular. Overall architectural style is neat, simple, using more new technologies, new structures, new materials, it is on behalf of the level of technological development of tea industry at that moment. Its interior design was used by large span and supported by 12 circular pillars. More valuable point is the new machinery room was equipped with the most traditional domestic Keemun-mounted production lines. These old tea making equipments have been well protected and properly used.

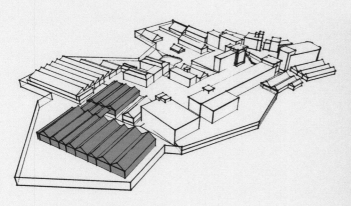

Former Warehouse for Preliminarily Processed Tea

老毛茶仓库

Built in 1951, this warehouse appears plain and simple, with grey brick walls, a roof consisting of three dual-pitched roofs, and a facade in the shape of the character ' 山 '. Inside the warehouse, running through the middle, is a corridor lined on each side with twelve identical storerooms, with floors and walls covered in Korean pine panels from Greater Khingan Range. There is a massive steelyard installed in the corridor. Those Korean pine panels retain a lingering aroma of tea.

老毛茶仓库建于 1951 年，为青砖墙体的库房建筑，由三个 " 人 " 字坡顶并联组成屋顶，外观正立面呈 " 山 " 字形，整体风格简洁明快。其室内相应为长廊居中，两侧分列 12 个尺度统一的内库房，其地板与四面壁板均为大兴安岭红松板材；长廊内现存大型过秤。那些与建筑同龄的红松板材，浸透并散发着让人难以忘怀的茶香。

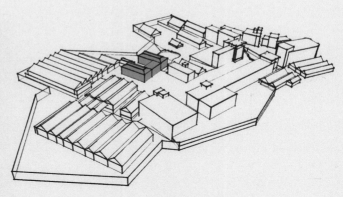

Manual Sorting Plant
手工拣厂

The manual sorting plant, a place of tea production in the stages of 'refinement', is a two-storied building, with the lower story being a spacious rectangular with glass windows in the four walls to provide natural lighting. Each of the slightly thin wood columns in the middle supports a crossbeam structure that comprises an upper and a lower wood slab, between them a grid of wooden bars, looking simple yet decoratively beautiful. Judging by these columns, the original building was a single-story one, to which a second story was later added for an increased scale of production, and the columns were erected for safety purposes.

手工拣厂是"精制工艺"阶段的生产场地，为二层楼建筑，下层室内矩形空间宽敞，四壁辟玻璃窗，采光明亮。居中一列略显细瘦的木柱上承横梁，而横梁由上下两层木板挟蜂巢状木格组成，具有简洁内敛且不失装饰性的美感。根据居中立柱分析，原设计为平房，后因生产规模扩大而加建上层，故为安全起见而增加立柱。

The facade of the quality control building, its beauty not faded by the passage of time.

时光的流逝，掩饰不住质检楼立面当年的精美。

Though the decorative railings now are covered in moss, their glossiness is reminiscent of the flourishing days of the tea factory.

尽管当年的花式栏杆已经被青苔覆盖，琉璃一般的色彩依然昭示着往昔的兴盛。

Built in 1953, the Workers' Center is clear and neat in style with a chaste facade, all its interior in a wood structure.

1953 年兴建的职工之家整体风格规整，立面简洁，内部采用全木质结构。

The office building has a veranda across its front, with its railing decoration and facade material both typical of the era.

办公楼采用外走廊的形式串联，栏杆花饰和立面选材都颇具时代特色。

池州为安徽省地级市，别名"秋浦"，地处长江南岸之
九华山地，下辖贵池区、东至县、石台县和青阳县，
北与安庆市隔江相望，南接黄山市，西南与江西省九
江市为邻。作为安徽省"两山一湖"（黄山、九华山、
太平湖）旅游区的重要组成部分和中国佛教四大名山
之一的九华山所在地，池州是长江下游地区重要的滨
江港口城市之一。

池州素有"千载诗人地"之誉，至今留有大量的名胜古
迹。自唐武德四年（621 年）正式设州置府，迄今近 1
400 年，而更早在南北朝时期，此地即为南梁昭明太子
萧统（501–531 年）封邑，他曾住此编选《昭明文选》，
这是中国现存最早的一部诗文总集；盛唐诗仙李白三上
九华、五游秋浦，留下《秋浦歌》等众多诗篇；晚唐杜
牧曾任池州刺史，所作的《清明》使杏花村闻名于世。
历代名人如陶渊明、苏轼、岳飞、陆游等都曾驻足池
州，书写下珍贵的历史篇章。而贵池傩戏、"京剧鼻祖"
青阳腔和东至花灯等一批国家级非物质文化遗产更名噪
一时。不过，在上述与池州历史相关的物质与非物质文
化遗产中，有一项或多或少是被世人所忽视的，即作为
祁红主要种植、加工地之一的池州。但值得庆幸的是，
这一缺憾于 2017 年 8 月后一步步得到了历史性的弥补。
2017 年 12 月 2 日，由中国文物学会、中国建筑学会主办
的"第二批中国 20 世纪建筑遗产项目发布暨池州生态
文明研究院成立仪式"在安徽省池州市举办。中国文物
学会会长单霁翔、中国建筑学会理事长修龙等百位学界
专家云集池州，在他们的见证下，位于池州的拥有 66
年历史的安徽国润茶业有限公司的祁门红茶老厂房 ——
贵池茶厂，入选"第二批中国 20 世纪建筑遗产名录"。
在此之前，安徽国润茶业有限公司的润思祁红制作技艺
还成功入选"安徽省第五批省级非物质文化遗产代表性
项目名录"。

在今长江南岸、池州市主城区（原贵池县）的西北一隅，
坐落着一组具有新中国成立初期时代特色的老工厂建筑
群。其毗邻池口码头的地理位置，令人不难推测出该老

The brownish red roof and the gray-blue
columns of stone form a harmonious sight.
Hanging beneath the wood beam later
added is an electric fan for the use of tea
processing workers.

棕红色的屋顶灰、青色的石柱构成一
幅和谐的画面，在一道后期添设的木
梁下吊起的，是专为下方制茶员工准
备的电扇。

Wen Yiduo (1899–1946) thought of tea drinking as the most important thing in his life. Tea is a yardstick of life, and it is a horrible thing to live without tea.

闻一多（1899–1946 年）将喝茶视为生活中最重要的事。茶是生活的尺度，缺少茶的日子不知如何过。

"In the summer of 1930," recalled Bing Xin, "Wen Yiduo and Liang Shiqiu came to visit my new home at Yenching University. I gave them both a cup of cold water, and all of sudden Wen Yiduo said, smiling, 'We'll be back in a minute'. They returned with a bag of tea, saying in a laugh that there should be cigarettes and tea to serve guests going forward ... Wen established for this newly formed family a 'custom' of entertaining guests with cigarettes and tea."

冰心在回忆中说，1930 年夏，闻一多与梁秋实到我们燕京大学的新居来看望，我给他们倒上两杯凉水，闻一多忽然笑着说"我们出去一会儿"。当他们回来时，拿来一包茶，笑着说，以后要准备茶烟待客 …… 闻一多为这个新成立的小家庭建立了一条烟茶待客的"风俗"。

Night shift workers just needed to pull the lamp cord to wen on to operate the machines

夕阳西下，晚班的茶工拽一下灯绳，便可继续进行机器的操作。

厂的产品大概是要经池口码头驶往长江航运线而发送外地的；厂区内呈锯齿形立面的老厂房，则为 20 世纪 50 年代苏式工业建筑的典型；距离锯齿形厂房不足一箭之地为工厂仓库，那里的每一间库房均是木板铺地、木质壁板环绕，观者至此无不被感染，每一块木板里都积存有浓郁的茶叶沁人心脾的馨香。至此，这座老厂房向世人揭示了它传奇般的身世：建于 1950 年的贵池茶厂，是属于农产品加工性质的制茶工厂。与此厂同时期同规模者，原本尚有祁门县祁门茶厂、东至县东至茶厂，但世事沧桑，时至今日而唯此独存。更珍贵的是，其前身就是同属池州地区范围的距离此地约 70 千米的原至德县尧渡街茶号 —— 余干臣创始祁门红茶的源头所在。

Double-crossbeam structures beneath the ceiling of the sorting plant, with the upper and lower crossbeams fastened with long bolts - between which is a grid of wooden bars. The slender wood columns stand slightly away from the middle, revealing the lightness of the structures.

拣厂采用了精致的双层木屋梁结构，中间用拼接好的木条斜撑，再用长螺栓进行固定。纤细的木柱亦巧妙地偏向一侧而非居中，尽显结构之轻盈。

On the surface of the machine base is written a line that reads 'Safety is for the sake of the revolution, the revolution is for the sake of safety'.

机器的底座上留有"安全为革命、革命促安全"字样，显示着长此以往的坚守。

现存主要由制茶车间、老毛茶仓库、手工拣厂等组成的原贵池茶厂老厂区，建筑实体为 1951 年始建，是新中国成立初期引进欧洲、苏联等国外建筑技术所建造的工业建筑佳作，其简洁的外观与实用功能自然融合，为存世较少的现代工业建筑实例，客观记录了新中国成立初期的经济状况和外贸策略 —— 农产品转向国营化生产，具有浓郁的现代工业建筑气息和现代建筑艺术风格，而其建筑功能却又是服务于古老的农产品加工的，寄托着几代人富国强民的理想。

On the one side of the sifting machine hang a dozen screens of different mesh sizes. Standing on a two-step wooden platform, a worker could the mesh screen easily.

分筛机一侧悬挂着十余片不同粗细的筛网，茶工们踩上木质的二层小台阶便可方便地对筛网进行更换

Chapter Two

Tea as a Messenger of Peace:
History of Keemun

In 1559, Venice published *Navigationi et Viaggi* (Navigations and Travels), a collection of Persian explorers' first-hand accounts of their travels, in which it was mentioned that "Chaicatai (the tea of China), in some cases dry and in other ones fresh, is boiled in water … The hotter, the better, when you drink it". This is perhaps the earliest record of tea in the West, but probably not of Western people accepting tea-drinking customs. The above-mentioned "dry" and "fresh" presumably refers to black tea and green tea. By the second half of the 17th century, tea had not only been accepted by China's neighbor Russia, it also found its way into the British royal family by way of the Netherlands, sweeping across Europe swiftly (tea was initially imported to Europe by the Dutch in 1606, and entered Britain in 1662). By then, tea gradually gained an equal position to cocoa and coffee, with Keemun beginning to ascend the stage for its particular quality.

篇二

烽烟国门下　茶香化干戈
——祁门红茶的前世今生

1559 年，威尼斯出版了一本波斯人写的《航海与旅行》："Chai catai（中国茶），它们有的是干的，有的是新鲜的，放在水中煮透……这种东西在喝的时候越烫越好。"这可能是西方对茶业最早的记载，但可能还不是西方人最早接受饮茶习俗的记录。此记录中，所谓"干的、新鲜的"，可能分指红茶、绿茶。至 17 世纪下半叶，茶叶不仅为毗邻中国的俄罗斯所接受，更经荷兰输入英国王室，迅速风靡欧洲（茶叶最初于 1606 年由荷兰引进欧洲大陆，1662 年进入英国）。至此，茶叶逐渐与可可、咖啡并列，以独特品质参与其中的祁门红茶就开始登上舞台。

Tea and Tea Culture
茶与茶文化

It is conservatively estimated that tea dates back more than 3,000 years in China. No later than 780, when *The Classic of Tea* by Lu Yu of the Tang dynasty appeared, tea-drinking became e a living habit and a cultural phenomenon peculiar to China, and began to spread worldwide. This monograph on tea not only recorded tea production and drinking before the Tang dynasty, but it also advocated a 'virtuous' view of tea, so that it became a symbol of Chinese culture itself, as did calligraphy and painting. After *The Classic of Tea*, Cai Xiang (1012–1067) of the Northern Song dynasty wrote *The Record of Tea* in the Huangyou era (1049–1053) of the dynasty. The most influential treatise on tea following *The Classic of Tea*, *The Record of Tea*, in two parts, talks about the color, aroma and taste of tea, the methods of tea boiling and drinking including storage, baking, pressing, sieving, boiling water, preheating, and tea spotting, and tea utensils like warmer, canister, hammer, clamps, grinder, sieve, vessel, spoon, and kettle.

Though the prevalent method of tea drinking in China today is to infuse tea (green tea or scented tea) in hot water, diverse ways of tea-drinking worldwide and their different cultural reflections may all be traced back to the place of origin of tea, China. In contrast to Chinese tea culture today, which highlights the enjoying of the delicate aroma of green tea often prepared with hot water, the ancient Chinese preferred to boil tea so that it would have a strong taste. The Chinese-style tea culture first spread to Korea, Vietnam, Japan among other neighboring countries and went on to find its way into Russia, India, and the Britain. In today's world, tea culture

In about 780, the first monograph on tea in the world, *The Classic of Tea*, appeared, which was a Chinese summation of tea at the time. Its author, Lu Yu (733-804), wrote the work in three volumes based on his collection of tea records, personal investigation and practical experience. It was the most thorough book on tea in ancient China, covering all aspects of tea during and before the Tang dynasty – history of tea, tea producing areas, and the function, planting, gathering and making, boiling, and drinking of tea.

公元 780 年左右，世界上最早的一部茶叶专著《茶经》问世这是当时中国关于茶的经验总结。作者陆羽 (733-804) 洋细收集历代茶叶史料，记述亲身调查和实践的经验，撰《茶经》三卷，对唐代及唐代以前的茶叶历史、产地、茶的功效、栽培、采制、煎煮、饮用的知识技术都作了阐达，是中国古代最完备的一部茶书。

may roughly be named after countries where tea-drinking has become a social custom and a cultural phenomenon, and such countries as Russia, the United Kingdom, Germany, the United States, Turkey, and Argentina may be seen as major branches of tea culture.

保守估计，中国人饮茶的历史至今已有 3 000 余年。至迟在公元 780 年唐代陆羽所著《茶经》问世之后，饮茶已成为中国特有的生活习惯和文化现象，并逐渐影响至全球。《茶经》不仅记载了唐代之前的中国茶叶生产、饮用的经验，更倡导、归纳出一种"精行俭德"的茶道精神，使得茶与中国书画等并列成为中国文化的象征。继《茶经》之后，北宋蔡襄（1012–1067）于北宋皇祐年间（1049–1053）著《茶录》，全书分上下篇论及色、香、味、藏茶、炙茶、碾茶、罗茶、候汤、熁盏、点茶等烹饮方法，以及茶焙、茶笼、砧椎、茶铃、茶碾、茶罗、茶盏、茶匙、汤瓶等器皿内容，是《茶经》之后最有影响的论茶专著。

虽然中国人如今的饮茶方式以沏泡清茶（绿茶、花茶）为主，但从全球范围来看，千差万别的饮茶方式及其所蕴含的不同的文化追求，都可在原产地中国找到源头。如当今的中国茶文化以品赏清淡幽香的绿茶为主，基本方式为热水冲泡，但在历史上，追求浓郁口感的煮茶饮用法。中国式的茶文化波及朝鲜、越南、日本等周边国家，后传入俄罗斯、印度、英国。当今世界，饮茶成为社会习俗并成为文化现象者，大致可按国家命名，俄罗斯、英国、德国、美国、土耳其、阿根廷等可称为重要的茶文化分支。

The Record of Tea, in two parts, was wrote in the Huangyou era (1049–1053) of the Northern Song dynasty 'due to the grace of His Highness'. It produced far-reaching influence in later ages. On the color of tea, he writes: 'The color of tea is most desirably white. But tea cakes are mostly coated with tea extracts, and thus there are blue, yellow, purple, and black tea cakes.' In expounding the aroma of tea, he writes: 'Tea has intrinsic aroma. But tribute tea manufacturers like to mix a small amount of Dryobalanops aromatica camphor, supposedly to enhance the aroma. The local people of Jian'an never mix any incense into tea, afraid to robe the natural aroma of tea.'

《茶录》作于北宋皇祐年间（1049–1053）
《茶录》一书为作者"承陛下知鉴"所作，分上下两篇，其论述对后世影响深远。如在论述茶色时，他说："茶色贵白，而饼茶大抵于表净膏泽，故有青、黄、紫、黑之异。"论述茶香时，他说："茶有真香，而入贡者，微以龙脑和膏以助香，建安民间试茶，皆不入香，恐夺其真。"

1. Russian Tea Culture
俄罗斯茶文化

Russia was the first country to import tea from China (according to records, the Russians were exposed to tea for the first time in about 1638). Unlike the Chinese, who preferred to infuse tea in hot water, the Russian people chose instead to boil tea, to which end they invented a tea boiler called the samovar. Tea thus prepared had a strong taste and was unavoidably bitter, and so they then added sugar, lemon juice and even milk.

俄罗斯是最早从中国传入茶叶的国家（据记载，俄罗斯人首次接触茶约在 1638 年）。俄罗斯人饮茶与中国区别较大，他们变中国本土流行的沏泡茶为煮茶，并发明了一种煮茶的工具——"茶炊"。而煮出来的茶虽浓郁，但难免苦涩，于是又在热茶汤中添加糖、柠檬汁乃至牛奶等。

Russian people enjoyed afternoon tea using a samovar. A unique symbol of Russian culture and art, a samovar doesn't take much time to boil tea, with water in it kept hot to make the taste of tea pleasantly strong. A small teapot is sometimes placed on top of a samovar, and Russian refreshments and fruit preserves are generally put around.

俄罗斯人用"茶炊"来享用下午茶。"茶炊"是俄罗斯独特的文化和艺术标志。这种茶具不需要花太多的时间来煮茶，其中的水也能够保持温度，使茶味香浓。"茶炊"上有时摆放小茶壶，周边一般会放有俄式点心和果酱。

2. British Tea Culture
英国茶文化

Catherine of Braganza drinking black tea in the royal palace of England.

在英格兰宫廷中饮用红茶的凯瑟琳。

A bit later than Russia, Britain began importing tea in the 1760s. By the 1850s, tea had become a popular drink across Britain, giving rise to the unique British tradition of afternoon tea. Tradition has it that Catherine of Braganza (1638–1705) was so fond of Chinese black tea that when she was married to the king of England, King Charles II, in her dowry were 221 pounds of black tea from Fujian, China, as well as all kinds of exquisite Chinese tea-things; in her time, black tea was seen as more valuable than silver. British poet Edmund Waller once wrote a poem in honor of this 'tea-drinking queen':

Venus her Myrtle, Phoebus has his bays;
Tea both excels, which she vouchsafes to praise.
The best of Queens, the best of herbs, we owe
To that bold nation which the way did show
To the fair region where the sun doth rise,
Whose rich productions we so justly prize.

With the royal family setting the trend, it naturally followed
that Britain became a big tea-drinking country. If we say that
coffee helped spawn critical thinking in France on literature,
art and philosophy, afternoon tea might have offered a source
of inspiration for British poetry and novels – tea played a part
in the lives of British literary giants Lord Byron, John Keats,
Jane Austen, and Charles Dickens.

英国略晚于俄罗斯，从 17 世纪 60 年代开始进口茶叶，
到 18 世纪 50 年代，茶叶已经变成英国人的全民饮料，
并由此派生出独特的英国 " 下午茶文化 "。相传葡萄牙
公主凯瑟琳（1638–1705）嗜饮中国红茶，于 1662 年嫁与
英国国王查理二世，她的嫁妆中包括 221 磅产自中国福
建的红茶及各种精美的中国茶具，而在那个时代，红茶
之贵重堪比银子。英国诗人埃德蒙 · 沃尔特曾作一首赞
美诗献给这位 " 饮茶王后 "：

维纳斯的香桃木和太阳神的月桂树，
都无法与王后称颂的茶叶媲美。
我们由衷感谢那个勇敢的民族，
因为他们给予了我们一位尊贵的王后
和一种最美妙的仙草，
并为我们指点通往繁荣之途。

有皇室引领风尚，英国成为饮茶大国似乎就顺理成章了。
如果说咖啡催生了法国的文艺与哲学思辨，则英式午茶
是其诗歌、小说的灵感策源 —— 有拜伦、济慈之诗意
盎然，有奥斯汀式的机智与优雅，也有狄更斯笔下的贫
街陋巷 ……

3. Turkish Tea Culture
土耳其茶文化

Tea produced in Turkey is a type of black tea. Turkey is a big tea consumer in the Islamic world, where people, like the Americans, think of tea and coffee as equally important. The Turkish people are very hospitable, and it is their tradition to invite friends to have tea. It is fair to say that Turkish tea culture displays the cultural characteristic of Turkish hospitality.

土耳其自产的茶叶属于红茶的一种。土耳其人与美国人相似，也是茶叶与咖啡并重，是伊斯兰教国家中的茶叶消费大国。土耳其人热情好客，请喝茶更是他们的一种传统习俗，也可以说，土耳其的茶文化展示着伊斯兰教国度热情好客的文化特色。

Black Tea and Black Tea Culture
红茶与红茶文化

In the tea world, two main tea cultures have been established based on which finished tea is preferred: On the is the green tea culture represented by the Chinese tea culture, which embodies a thousand-year-old *gengdu* (cultivate-and-read) tradition and *pinming* (tea tasting) of an Oriental poetic nature; the other is the British and Russian tea cultures in which black tea (including semi-fermented black tea), formed to suit extremely cold climate and echo post-Industrial Revolution pursuits of high culture.

按照茶叶的成品分类，茶文化的世界形成了两大门派：以中国茶文化为代表的绿茶文化 —— 延绵数千年的耕读传统与东方诗意性的 " 品茗 "；以红茶（含半红茶）为主的英国、俄罗斯茶文化 —— 适应高寒地带的浓郁与工业革命之后人们对优雅文化的追求。

1. Chinese Tea Culture Focused on Green Tea
以绿茶为主的中国茶文化

The Chinese don't simply drink green tea, with many preferring scented tea instead. Semi-fermented black tea (represented by oolong of Fujian, pu'er of Yunnan, etc.) and totally fermented black tea (most notably Wuyi tea of Fujian) are also quite popular, and there also semi-fermented tea cakes (milk tea, highland barley tea, etc.) largely consumed in the pasturing areas of Inner Mongolia, Tibet, and Xinjiang. Even in the world of pure green tea, there are many varieties each of which is in some way different from another, such as Longjing tea, Biluochun, Huangshan Maofeng tea, Lu'an Melon Seed,

and Junshan Yinzhen. But overall, enjoying the pure natural taste of green tea, and feeling the gift of nature and the world as it is, are what is at the heart of Chinese tea culture.

A portrait of early 19th-century English poet Lord Byron (left) and Don Juan played by a Chinese actor on the opera stage.

英国 19 世纪初诗人拜伦肖像及中国演唱者在歌剧舞台上所扮演的唐璜形象。

中国并不纯饮绿茶，饮用衍生品花茶的消费数额也未必少于绿茶，而半发酵性质的半红茶（以福建乌龙茶、云南普洱茶等为代表）与全发酵性质的红茶（以福建武夷山岩茶为代表）也甚为流行，更有内蒙古、西藏、新疆等地的牧区主要消费半发酵的茶砖（奶茶、青稞茶等）。即使在纯粹绿茶的世界里，又有西湖龙井、碧螺春、黄山毛峰、六安瓜片、君山银针等有着微妙差异的诸多品种。但总体说，欣赏绿茶的纯天然味，从中体会大自然的恩赐与人世百态，是中国茶文化的根本。

2. British and Russian Tea Cultures Focused on Black Tea
以红茶为主的英国、俄罗斯茶文化

Britain, Russia and other tea-drinking countries favor black tea, but they don't reject other varieties of tea either. The essential point, however, lies in a strong taste of tea as necessitated by a cold climate as well as in a cultural life sparked by drinking tea at leisure outside of necessary material life. Below is a verse from *Eugene Onegin*, a masterpiece of famous Russian poet Alexander Pushkin:

'Twas dusk! Upon the table bright
Shrill sang the samovar at eve,
The china teapot too ye might
In clouds of steam above perceive.
Into the cups already sped
By Olga's hand distributed
The fragrant tea in darkling stream,
…

In Russia, the intrinsic fragrance of tea from China was preserved, but the appearance of samovars shaped a different tea culture than the Chinese way of tea drinking. Among other Russian figures, Leo Tolstoy, Anton Chekhov, Maxim Gorky, Pyotr Ilyich Tchaikovsky, and Ilya Repin all conceived, in such a tea culture, ideas that resulted in their masterpieces.

Unlike Russia, Britain represents another major branch of tea culture, where afternoon tea helped give rise to the famous works of novelist Jane Austen and poets Lord Byron, John Keats and Jane Austen. In *Don Juan*, one of his masterpieces, Lord Byron writes:

I feel my heart become so sympathetic,
That I must have recourse to black Bohea;
'T is pity wine should be so deleterious …

"Black Bohea" mentioned in above verse refers to the black tea that China produced in the late Qing dynasty specifically to be exported. Chinese tea made contributions to these two cultural powers.

同样，英国、俄罗斯等国家以饮用红茶为主，但也并不排斥其他。不过，其根本的着眼点，在于高寒地带所需要的浓郁，以及物质生活必需之余由品茶而引发的文化生活。俄罗斯大诗人普希金名作《叶甫盖尼·奥涅金》中有这样的诗句：

There are accounts in Western records of the sale of Chinese black tea abroad.

对于中国红茶的外销，西方人在他们的书籍中也有所记录。

In his book *All about Tea*, William H. Ukers recorded, in the 'A Chronology of Tea' section, that 'An Edinburgh goldsmith advertises green tea for sale at sixteen shillings a pound and black at thirty shillings.' British biographer Mary Shelley recorded black tea for sale at twenty shillings to three shillings a pound at the time. Because of its strong and particular taste, Chinese black tea was quite popular on international markets and sold as far as Britain, the Netherlands and France, among other places. Englishman Norton praised black tea, saying 'drinking this tea is better than drinking ginseng soup.'

据尤克斯《茶叶全书》中的"茶叶年表"所记述，1705 年，爱丁堡金匠刊登广告，绿茶（GreenTea）每磅售十六先令，红茶（BlackTea）三十先令。英国传记作家玛丽返蓝尼夫人记录，当时茶价为红茶二十至三十先令。由于中国红茶茶味浓郁、独特，在国际市场上备受欢迎，远销英国、荷兰、法国等地。英国人诺顿夸奖说："喝这种茶胜过饮人参汤。"

Cups of Keemun on a blue-and-white saucer.
青花瓷茶托上的祁红。

天色转黑，晚茶的茶炊
闪闪发亮，在桌上咝咝响，
它烫着瓷壶里的茶水；
薄薄的水雾在四周荡漾。
这时已经从奥尔加的手下
斟出了一杯又一杯的香茶，
浓酽的茶叶在不停地流淌
……

从中国舶来的茶在俄罗斯保持了本质的清香，但异域的
茶炊却展示着与本土茶饮相比微妙别样的茶文化氛围。
之后的托尔斯泰、契诃夫、高尔基以及音乐家柴可夫斯基、
画家列宾等，无一不从这种文化氛围中孕育其传世之作。

英国不同于俄罗斯，是茶文化的另一个重要分支 ——
英式午茶所派生出来的奥斯汀式的美文与拜伦、济慈、
雪莱的诗歌。拜伦（George Gordon Byron，1788–1824）
在其代表作《唐璜》中写道：

> 我觉得我的心儿变得那么富于同情，
> 我一定要去求助于武夷的红茶（Black Bohea）；
> 真可惜，酒却是那么的有害……

诗中提到的"武夷的红茶"，系指晚清时期中国专为应
付外销市场而生产的专供出口的红茶。中国茶为这两个
文化大国做出了贡献。

The Birth of Chinese Black Tea for Sale Abroad
中国外销红茶的诞生

1. Tea Introduction to and Cultivation in the West
西方人对茶的引进与培植

While tea consumed in such European countries as Russia and Britain originated in China as early as the Tang dynasty, tea was not popular across Europe until after the Ming dynasty, about four to five hundred years ago, and from then on there developed the Russian way of tea boiling and the English morning tea, afternoon tea, and evening tea drinking customs. Tea initially consumed in Europe was largely semi-fermented tea cakes and totally-fermented Wuyi tea from China.

俄罗斯、英国等欧洲国家所饮之茶，最初由中国而来，历史可上溯至唐代，但真正风靡欧洲则在明代之后，距今约四百年左右，并形成欧洲以俄罗斯为代表的茶厨煮茶方式和英国的"晨茶·午茶·晚茶"饮茶习惯。初期使用的茶叶，基本上是半发酵的中国茶砖和全发酵的武夷山红茶。

A huge and almost irreversible trade deficit caused by tea trade is also considered to have been one of the reasons for the Opium Wars.

因茶叶交易而带来的巨大的几乎无可逆转的贸易逆差，也被认为是鸦片战争爆发的原因之一

Vessels sailing across the oceans for trade in the East (top) and crowds waiting for goods from the East at a port (bottom).

远渡重洋到东方进行贸易的船只及港口期待东方贸易品的民众。

2. The Birth of Chinese Black Tea Specifically for Sale Abroad
中国纯外销型红茶的诞生

Black tea was invented by accident in China during the Ming dynasty. Legend has it that, sometime in the mid to later Ming dynasty, it was the tea-gathering season in a place called Tongmu in the Wuyi Mountains region of Chong'an, Fujian Province, and when a tea farmer found that the tea leaves he gathered and failed to process the day before had fermented, to save losses he baked the tea leaves with masson pine firewood and used some special processes to maximally preserve the tea ingredients – his attempt resulting in the earliest black tea in China. At the time, black teadidn't win favour on the domestic market dominated by green tea, but after the Dutch merchants

Though modern people use different tea utensils to ancient people, to Keemun lovers, nothing has ever changed.

虽然现代人所用的茶具与古代不一而同，但对于祁门红茶的热爱未尝有丝毫改变。

Chinese writer Ba Jin (1904–2005), acclaimed as 'the conscience of the 20th century', saw drinking tea as an essential part of his life.

百年人生，当属始终如一杯温暖茶的巴金（1904–2005），从文化传统到生活习惯，一生与茶息息相关，他被誉为"二十世纪的良心"。

Drinking tea since childhood, he was fond of *tuocha* (a compressed tea variety) and black tea, and had a wife who was good at making tea. A 'new' Shanghai and an 'old' Chengdu are often seen as a point of departure by which to study his literary legacies. In his correspondence in 1958 with his wife Xiao Shan revealed their 'tea' life. In his letter to Xiao Shan on January 27, Ba Jin said that he bought a quarter of a kilogram of Dianhong tea and half a kilogram of Indian coffee, and asked if Xiao Shan wanted some Keemun. In her letter in reply, Xiao Shan wrote that she had bought black tea, too, from a department store, of two varieties – one at a price of nine *jiao* and the other at five *jiao*, either in six hundred grams, and asked Ba Jin to decide whether or not to buy Keemun. A week later, she suggested in another letter that if there was good black tea in Beijing he should get some.

巴金从小喝茶，日常生活中爱喝沱茶、红茶，还娶了位擅长泡茶的太太萧珊。在巴金身上，上海的新和成都的旧"是人们审视他文学遗产的切入点。1958 年的一则巴金与萧珊的书信传达了他们的"茶"生活。是年 1 月 27 日，在写给萧珊的信中，巴金说他买了半斤滇红和一斤印度咖啡，问萧珊是否要买祁门红茶等。萧珊回信说，她也买了红茶，是在百货公司买的，有两种价，一种九角，一种五角，每样买了六两，买不买祁门红茶，让巴金做主。一周后，萧珊信中再说，北京有好红茶，不妨再带些。

took it back to Europe in around 1604, black tea soon gained popularity with the English royal family and even across all of Europe, giving birth to the 'afternoon tea' tradition that has continued to this day.

As early as before the First Opium War, Englishmen already began trying to cultivate tea trees in Assam, India and, through repeated experiments, produced a small amount of black tea in 1836, and expanded production thereafter. Black tea produced in India then was still far from able to supersede Chinese tea, neither quantitatively nor qualitatively. By 1888 after the Second Opium War, Indian tea had increased both quantitatively and qualitatively, and because Wuyi tea – China's leading export then – was not adequate in output and quality to meet market demand, India for the first time topped China in terms of black tea exports to Britain. Perhaps it was against such a backdrop that Keemun was born in Anhui.

中国在明代开始产生红茶，说起来倒是有个意外。相传明朝中后期的某年，地处武夷山区的福建省崇安县桐木地区在采茶的季节，当天已采摘的茶青因故没有来得及制作茶叶，第二天已经发酵。为了挽回损失，茶农以当地马尾松干柴进行炭焙烘干，并通过增加一些特殊工序，以最大程度保证茶叶成分。这种为补救过失所制的茶叶即中国最初的红茶制品。这种红茶在国内并不能撼动绿茶市场，但 16 世纪末 17 世纪初（约 1604 年）由荷兰商人带入欧洲，却随即风靡英国皇室乃至整个欧洲，并掀起流传至今的"下午茶"风尚。

早在鸦片战争之前，英国人已经开始在印度阿萨姆设茶叶种植园尝试种植茶树，经反复试验，于 1836 年可以生产出少量红茶，并逐年扩大生产。但这时的印度出品红茶无论数量还是质量，还远不能取代中国茶叶。至鸦片战争后的 1888 年，印度茶叶生产数量及产品质量都有了长足进展，而中国原本主打的武夷岩茶的产量和质量不足以保证市场需求，因而印度出口至英国的红茶产品首次超过了中国。或许，这是安徽祁红"出生"的背景。

Chinese writer Yu Dafu (1896–1945) was a tea lover, many characters from his pen had a bond with tea.

人间有茶便销魂的郁达夫（1896–1945），在其笔下有很多的人有茶的"歌唱"。

When he took a cup of tea, his hero took a cup of tea, too; when he put it down, his hero put it down, and when he finished tea and got out, his story came to the end. While others wrote about the lofty lightness of tea, he wrote about the desirousness of tea. While others wrote about the leisurely comfort of fooling around at a tea house, he wrote about the laziness of tea house patrons. While others wrote about the wild appeal of having tea in a mountain, he wrote about the untroubled ease of it.

他端起茶杯，笔下人物也端起茶杯，他放下茶杯，笔下人物也放下茶杯，他喝完茶出门，故事也到了尾声。别人写茶的清淡，他写茶的欲望。别人写泡茶馆的闲适，他写泡茶馆人士的懒散。别人写山中茶的野趣，他写山中茶的逍遥。

Chapter Three

Born at Yaodu and Innovated in New China: Founding of Guorun Tea Industrial Co., Ltd.

To educate with tea and to edify with culture occupies an important position in the development course of Guorun Keemun. A quote from the *Records of the Grand Historian* by Sima Qian says, 'the people are most important to the king as food to the people', which shows the importance of food from the perspective of fighting a war. With people's needs for food and clothing basically met, this view has new implications when it comes to the personnel and events related to tea. Today, when savouring a cup of Keemun in an elegant and quiet teahouse and enjoying the wonderful tea aroma, do you think of the arduous journey the pioneers went through in developing the Keemun? Here you will see the list of major contributions made by the founders like Yu Ganchen (1850–1920) and Hu Yuanlong (1836–1924) and the gold medal fetched from the 1915 Panama International Exposition that made Keemun shoot to fame around the world.

篇三

创始在尧渡　创新在共和
——国润茶业的创业

以茶育人，以文化人，在"国润祁红"发展史上占重
要位置。司马迁在《史记》中云"王者以民人为天，
而民人以食为天"，这是从战争胜负视角论述粮食
重要性的。在基本解决温饱问题的情况下，用此论
断看茶人茶事有它新的含义。今天，人们在深处优
雅宁静的茶室，静静品一杯祁红，感悟茶香妙境时，
是否知道曾经的前辈们为祁红经历了怎样艰难的发
展历程？这里有祁红创始人余干臣（1850–1920）、
胡元龙（1836–1924）的贡献榜，更有使祁红在国
际上声名鹊起的 1915 年祁红巴拿马万国博览会捧
回的金质奖章。

CHINA'S TEA BUSINESS URGENTLY NEEDED AN OPPORTUNITY to renew itself, and the opportunity for turnaround came unexpectedly. Keemun came to be exported at the right time and soon became the second best-selling tea for export after Wuyishan black tea. Here we must mention the Keemun founder Yu Ganchen (about 1850–1920), also named Changkai, native to Yi County of Huizhou, Anhui, who served as a taxation officer in Fuzhou for a good seven years. Though in the low position of a taxation officer, Yu Ganchen in Fuzou (home to the then-largest tea exporting port in the country) often engaged in major economic and trade affairs vital to common people's livelihood; he made friends with the heads of various associations and guilds like *Gong Yi Tang* which mainly dealt in black tea; and he often headed to black tea production areas in Fujian. He thereforee had a good understanding about black tea production, and knew well that the sales of black tea would be brisk and lucrative, and could be a pillar for the country's economic development. In 1869, the Fuzhou tea community collectively protested against the foreign black tea purchasers beating down prices, and entreated the government to defer tea taxation. Though Yu Ganchen, a witness to and participant in the whole process, suggested ways to cope with the foreign purchasers, his words carried little weight. In 1874 he was dismissed.

A portrait of Yu Ganchen.

余干臣画像。

In the first year of the Guangxu Reign (1875), Yu Ganchen who had always showed concern for state affairs, returned back to his hometown, in a humble position. Knowing very well that good tea grew in a good environment, he paid attention to all related things on his homeward journey and found the soil in Huizhou and Chizhou, as well as the surrounding areas, was rich in organic matter and the tea in the region was mostly of the paper mulberry leaf species with thick leaves, suitable for being made into quality black tea. He thene started a trial production of black tea in his hometown. The product looked tight and even, black and lustrous. When the tea was brewed, Yu Ganchen was amazed by the extraordinary mellow fragrance, which he had never experienced before. There was a floral, fruity and honey-like aroma from bright red infusion. Right away Yu Ganchen had the tea sent to Fuzhou. As he had expected, his friends engaging in tea business in Fuzhou were also deeply impressed by the bright red colour and mellow fragrance and suggested that he should put it in mass production. After field investigation, Yu Ganchen set up the black tea store at Yaodu Street in Jiande County (today's Dongzhi), a tea production area, and started to make Congou black tea by using local materials.

Yaodu Street is in the valley of Yaodu River, flanked by grotesque mountains with old trees and bamboo groves, and tea gardens scattered around. When Yu Ganchen, who had read extensively since childhood, came to this, rich land that had fostered many talents, he naturally remembered *The Ode to the Good Tea in the South,* written by Mei Raochen while serving as County Head in the area in the Northern Song Dynasty. He promptly founded a store, recruited apprentices,

The bright red infusion of Keemun black tea.

祁门红茶红艳明亮的茶汤。

purchased fresh tea leaves, and invited Shu Jining from Ningzhou to make black tea, in light his experience of making Ningzhou black tea. As thus he pioneered the endeavour of making black tea, which he himself knew well. It turned out that the newcomer even outshined Wuyishan black tea.

Notably, Yu Ganchen had an open mind rare among common merchants. He was not a conservative Anhui merchant. He hoped that the techniques of making black tea under his guidance could benefit not only himself, but more importantly his hometown and his country. He imparted the otherwise secret recipe of black tea production to many people for free, like Hong Fangren and Liu Chun, who accompanied him on his homeward journey and acted as his guides. In the following year of 1876, he suggested that Hu Yuanlong, native to Qimen, should build Rishun Tea Factory at *Pei Gui Shan Fang*. His excellent apprentice Chen Shanghao returned back to his home village of Zhengchong to run Shanghaofang Tea Shop, with complete mastery of related skills and techniques for making black tea. Yu Ganchen was an enkindler. The little spark of this new black tea made a great fire in the region. His homeward journey became a way of exploration and discovery, leaving behind an unparalleled black tea belt with mellow fragrance. Soon afterwards, the black tea produced from Qimen under Huizhou, Guichi (today's

Chizhou), Dongzhi under Chizhou, Shitai under Chizhou, Yi
County under Huizhou and Fuliang of Jiangxi under Jingdezhen
is all referred to as Keemun black tea.

Later, Keemun black tea went beyond Anhui and travelled
across the ocean to reach the British Isles, and become the
favorite beverage of the queen and the royal family. Thus the
British-style afternoon tea became popular in Britain, and
it was famed as the noblest black tea and the tea of teas. In
competition against the black tea of India and that of Sri Lanka,
Keemun black tea won the gold medal at Panama International
Exposition in 1915, the fourth year for the Republic of China,
and became one of the world's three high-aroma black teas,
with the other two being Darjeeling black tea of India and
Uva black tea of Sri Lanka. Keemun thus won the fame as the
tea of teas. The Chinese black tea regained fame and market,
which marked China succeeded in fighting against the Western
trade monopoly. In the 1930s, a small amount of Keemun
originally produced for export was sold in China. Some of the
intellectuals who had been studying in Europe and America,
and Chinese senior businessmen who had been long getting
along with foreign merchants, began to bring the British-style
afternoon tea into their homes as a new fashion, with their

Runsi Keemun Manual Tea-Making
Factory completed in 1962.

1962 年竣工的润思祁红手工拣厂。

Old photo of the Panama –
Pacific International Exposition
held in San Francisco in 1915.

1915 年在旧金山召开的巴拿
马—太平洋国际博览会旧影。

growing understanding of European and American culture.

On an autumn day of 2014, the famous painter Li Xiaoke, son of Li Keran, walked into the Clement afternoon tea salon in Shanghai to talk about the days of 'co-habiting' with such masters as Xu Beihong, Qi Baishi, Lin Fengmian, Li Kuchan, Dong Xiwen, Wu Guanzhong and Dong Yongyu in the dormitory for the faculty of the Central Academy of Fine Arts at Dayabao Alleyway in Beijing. Besides Li Xiaoke, the descendants of Ai Qing, Wu Zuguang, Lu Yanshao and Xie Yaliu were also there. The tea culture among them corroborates the philosophy of the elder generation of masters and it can never be affected. To play a part in the cultural community is to exert subtle influence and let nature take its course. In the years of Westernization, the ladies of extraordinary deportment who were deeply influenced by foreign styles hosted tea parties or salons at home. For example, the 'Madam's Salon' hosted by Lin Huiyin was very famous and quite influential among the intellectuals in Beijing. According to the recollection of related people, the family salon of Liang Sicheng kept the habit of starting to drink tea at half past four every afternoon. Naturally Lin Huiyin was the center of the party while Liang Sicheng had few words, but from time to time he expressed a few simple but humorous utterances. Whatever Lin Huiyin talked

Opening Ceremony of the Exposition.

展会开幕式。

The banquet in honor of the Chinese delegation during the Exposition.

展会中招待中国代表团的宴会。

Gold Medal from the Exposition.

展会金奖奖牌。

Entrance to China's Pavilion

中国馆入口。

about was always lively and interesting. On this point, I think of Lin Huiyin's words in *Kunming Teahouse,* recording the days of Liang and Lin in the Southwest Associated University:

It is a multi-dimensional painting
of many faces
in the teahouse of the Shuncheng Street
amid the hubbub.
Various postures. Life
depicts different dimensions.
Seats are fully occupied. Some are smiling,
some frowning, and some smoking.

Anhui Guorun Tea Industrial Co., Ltd. (Guorun Tea Business)
is a famous tea group company which integrates tea planting,
processing, brand operation and international trade. The
company as well as its products is in the same line as the tea
store on Yaodu Street run by Yu Ganchen.

In 1950 the South Anhui Branch of COFCO set up
Guichi Tea Factory, a large new-style machine-based tea
factory, at Chikou Village, Guichi County (today's 33, Chikou
Road, Chikou City). Afterwards, the Yu Ganchen Tea Store,
Tongchun Tea Store and many other private time-honored
Keemun tea stores on Yaodu Street were nationalized, with the
traditional manual tea-making techniques retained.

Guorun Tea Industrial Co., Ltd. with its Runsi Keemun
being the most authentic modern version of Yu Ganchen
Keemun has been all along a flag in China's business
community. But after the war, the tea store at Yaodu Street
came to a standstill.

中国茶叶界亟待一个重整旗鼓的转机，而这个转机也
不期而至了 —— 祁门红茶适时加入到了外销红茶阵营，
并很快继武夷山红茶之后，成为外销的主力。这里，
要提及祁红的创始人余干臣（约 1850–1920）。余干臣，
名昌恺，安徽徽州黟县人士，曾任福州府税课司大使
达七年之久。虽然税课司大使仅仅是九品小吏，但因
福州是当时全国最大的茶叶出口口岸，故余干臣经常
参与到涉及民生的经贸要务。他在任内作为税务官员
与以经营红茶为主的公义堂等行帮会首结为朋友，经
常前往福建红茶产地，对红茶生产有了明确的了解，
深知红茶畅销利厚，为国家重要的经济支柱。1869 年，
福州茶帮集体抗议洋商压价采购，同时请求政府允许
缓缴茶叶税收。亲眼目睹并参与其事的余干臣，虽建
言应对外商的蓄意压价，但无奈官卑言轻，在 1874 年
遭罢官变故。

光绪元年（1875 年），"位卑未敢忘忧国"的余干臣自
福建回乡，他深知"好山好水出好茶"的道理，处处留

意，于是在途中发现家乡（徽州、池州一带）土壤富含有机物，所产茶叶多系楮叶种，叶质肥厚，似乎很适于加工成优质红茶，于是在家乡开始了试制。所制茶叶外形紧细匀整，色泽乌润，当第一批红茶入杯冲泡时，余干臣被那一股从未有过的奇异醇香深深地震撼了，那是一种特有的似花似果似蜜的香气，汤色红艳明亮。余干臣当即让人将红茶捎往福州，如他所料，福州茶帮朋友也被此茶红亮的汤色、沉韵的醇香所震撼，即刻向他建议批量生产。于是，经实地考察，余干臣在产茶区建德县（今东至）尧渡街设红茶庄，开始正式以本地原料仿制工夫红茶。

尧渡街地处尧渡河谷，奇峰叠嶂，古树竹海，乡野散布着茶香弥漫的茶树园。幼读诗书的余干臣至此人杰地灵之地，自然联想到北宋梅尧臣在此任县令时所作《南有嘉茗赋》，他当即置办门面，收徒设店，收购鲜叶，并延请宁州师傅舒基立按宁红经验试制红茶，开创性地做起了他所知晓的红茶。与武夷山红茶相比，不啻青出于蓝。

尤为难能可贵的是，余干臣天生具有一般商人所不具备的更为开阔的襟怀：他不是一个保守的传统徽商，他希望他所掌握的红茶技艺不仅令个人受益，更要造福桑梓故里，乃至邦国。他把原本属于独家秘笈的红茶制作方法无偿传授给了更多的人，如陪同他回乡并兼任向导的洪方仁、刘春，并在次年（1876 年）建议祁门人士胡元龙在培桂山房筹建日顺茶厂，而得意门生陈尚好多年以后学技精湛，也回到自己家乡正冲村自办尚好坊茶号。如同一个播火者，余干臣使这一地区的红茶新品在这一带呈现星火燎原之势，他的回乡之路成为一条探索发现之路，为后人留下了一条幽香甜醇、绝世无双的红丝带。不久，这款在安徽省祁门（徽州辖县）、贵池（今池州市）、东至（池州辖县）、石台（池州辖县）、黟县（徽州辖县），以及江西浮梁（景德镇市辖县）一带均有出产的红茶，而被统称为"祁门红茶"。

不久，祁门红茶穿过蜿蜒曲折的徽商故道，越过重洋，传到英伦三岛，成为英国女王和王室的至爱饮品，由此演绎出风靡欧洲的英式"下午茶"，被誉为"红茶皇后""茶中英豪"。自此，在与印度红茶、斯里兰卡红茶的竞争中，祁门红茶于民国 4 年（1915 年）获巴拿马万国博览会的金质奖章，由此与印度大吉岭红茶、斯里兰卡乌龙茶并称"世界三大高香红茶"，祁红赢得"茶中英豪"的美称，中国红茶重新赢得声誉和市场，宣告了中国反西方贸易垄断的意图获得成功。在 20 世纪 30 年代，祁红也有少量的"出口转内销"现象。一些留学欧美的知识分子及与外商长期打交道的中国工商界高层人士，随着对欧美文化认识的加深，也开始将英式"下午茶"作为新的时尚的生活方式引进家中。

2014 年秋季某日，李可染之子、著名画家李小可走进上海克勒门下午茶沙龙，畅谈在北京大雅宝胡同中央美院教职工宿舍与徐悲鸿、齐白石、林风眠、李苦禅、董希

Li Shutong (1880–1942) still wearing the makeup for playing the role of Marguerite in *La Traviata* poses for a group photo with his classmates.

出演《茶花女》女主角玛格丽特后尚未卸妆的李叔同（1880–1942）与同学合影

To speak from the angle of tea, Li Shutong was born in the tea sale area of Tianjin and died in the tea production area of Fujian. He seemed destined to be associated with tea such that Lin Yutang from Zhangzhou, also a tea production place near Quanzhou, said, "Li Shutong is one of the few top geniuses of our generation, and the most exceptional individual." In 1905 Li Shutong went to Japan to study music, painting and drama, and founded a drama club. To raise money, he dressed himself as a woman to play the role of Marguerite in *La Traviata*. Someone remarked that in the first half of his life Li Shutong was an exceptionallytalented man, and he was the compassionate Monk Hongyi, versed in the Buddhist sutras in the latter half of his life (since 1918).

从茶的角度看，他生在茶销区天津，圆寂于茶乡福建，仿佛宿命般与茶有不可割舍的关系，以至于泉州不远的产茶区漳州人林语堂说："李叔同是我们时代最有才华的几位天才之一，也是最奇特的一个人，最遗世而独立的一个人。1905年李叔同东渡日本学习音乐、绘画和戏剧，创办戏剧社。为筹集善款，他男扮女装，出演《茶花女》女主角玛格丽特。有人评价，李叔同前半生是走路都掉才华的人，而称弘一法师的后半生（1918年后），则是精研律宗的慈悲僧人。

文、吴冠中、董永玉等大师"同居"的日子，同来的还
有艾青、吴祖光、陆俨少、谢雅柳等人的后代们。茶友
的茶文化是印证老一辈文化大家理念的文化，永远无法
刻意；做文化，就要以文化之，水到渠成。西风东渐的
年月，中国风华绝代的洋派女士们当仁不让地主持着自
己的茶聚或沙龙，如林徽因"太太的客厅"声名最为响
亮，在北平文化圈内颇具影响力。据后人回忆，20 世纪
30 年代梁思成的家庭沙龙，延续着每天下午 4 点半开始
喝茶的习惯。林徽因自然是茶会的中心，梁思成则说话
不多，偶尔插一两句话，很简洁也很生动诙谐，而林徽
因则不管议到什么话题则总可引人入胜，生动活泼。此
时，让人回忆起梁、林在西南联大，林徽因对《昆明茶馆》
的描述：

> 这是立体的构画，
> 描在这里许多样脸，
> 在顺城脚的茶铺里
> 隐隐起喧腾声一片。
> 各种的姿势，生活
> 刻画着不同方面：
> 茶座上全坐满了，笑的，
> 皱眉的，有的抽着旱烟。

今日的安徽国润茶业有限公司（简称"国润茶业"）是国内知名的一家集茶叶种植、加工、品牌运营和国际贸易于一体的茶叶集团企业。从历史沿革上说，国润茶业有限公司及其产品，与余干臣开设尧渡街茶号正是一脉相承。

1950 年，中国茶叶公司皖南分公司在贵池县池口村（今池州市池口路 33 号）筹建大型新式机制茶厂 —— 贵池茶厂。之后，国家对尧渡街余干臣茶号、同春茶号等多家私营祁红老茶号进行了国营化改造，并保存了手工制茶传统工艺。

国润茶业有限公司及其名下的润思祁红，在谱系上确系最正宗的余干臣祁红之嫡传，一直是中国民族工商业界的一面旗帜，但抗战后，尧渡街茶号处于停产状态。

A Bird's Eye View of Guorun Tea Factory.
国润茶厂鸟瞰图。

Chapter Four

Green Mountains still Remain, and Tea Aroma Is More Mellow: Inheritance and Innovation of Qimen Black Tea

Since the beginning of Qimen black tea, many tea bases and manufacturers have been developed in Huizhou and Chizhou of Anhui Province. With the times changing, most of the te- growing bases are still extant, while many factories have been closed. Up to now, Anhui Guorun Tea Industry Co., Ltd. in Chizhou is the main factory that can still maintain a considerable scale. From Guichi Tea Factory to today's Guorun Qimen black tea, the history and changes of the factory profoundly reflect the evolution history of Qimen black tea from the late Qing Dynasty to the Republic of China. From the manual workshop built in early 1875 to the national factory built in the early 1950s, Guorun Qimen black tea has become a 'living heritage' classic, with abundant stories to tell. It is a 'living' point in efforts to promote Chizhou culture. This old factory building is a shell, while the traditional craft is the soul, housing the dazzling cultural symbol of Chizhou, and presenting the spirit of Chinese culture to the world.

篇四

青山依旧在　醇香胜往昔：
祁红时光的传承与创新

自祁门红茶问世以来，安徽徽州、池州一带曾有多个种茶基地与厂商。随着时代变换，种茶基地大多保留至今，而工厂则多有凋零。至今仍能保持相当规模者，主要为池州的安徽国润茶业有限公司。从贵池茶厂到今日国润祁红，其历程与变迁深刻地反映了晚清民国到现在中国祁红茶的演变史。从1875年初建的手工作坊到20世纪50年代初国家建厂，"国润祁红"成为"活态遗产"传承经典，有丰富的故事可讲，它是做好文化池州大文章的活态点。这座老厂房是"躯壳"，传统工艺是灵魂，留存的是池州耀眼的文化符号，是中国走向世界茶文化的灵气与文化品质。

Tea leaves that have not yet been put into storage are piled up in the factory building, their warm orange colour echoing the cool and refreshing colour of the factory building. These packaged tea leaves are being transported from place to place every day, vividly portraying the tea factory as living heritage.

厂房内堆有尚未入库的茶叶，温润的橙色与厂房的清冷遥相呼应。这些成包的茶叶每天都在来往搬运，是茶厂成为活态遗产的真实写照。

AFTER 1949, FOLLOWING A LONG WAR, PEOPLE LIVED in destitution and we had to start from scratch. In order to resume production in a short period of time, the state turned its attention to the traditional large foreign exchange earner – Qimen black tea in Anhui.

However, the situation was extremely grim. Firstly, as Huizhou and Chizhou in Anhui Province were devastated by the war, tea gardens declined and more than half of the tea-making workshops were closed down. Secondly, after a 13-year pause from 1937, most of the traditional tea importers in Europe and America turned to other tea-producing countries. Thirdly, even if former workshop production was resumed, the output would not be sufficient to meet the demand of the expanding international market. Therefore, the country was to resume Qimen black tea's production and export at all costs, and implement Qimen black tea's industrial production on the basis of the traditional workshop style.

1949 年后，中国面临久经战乱而民生凋敝、百废待兴的局面，为了在短时间内恢复生产，在安徽，国家把目光投向了传统的创汇大户 —— 祁门红茶。

然而，形势异常严峻：其一，盛产祁红的安徽徽州、池州一带，因战争重创，茶园凋零，制茶作坊倒闭大半；其二，经 1937 年之后长达 13 年的停顿，欧美等传统的茶叶输入大户多半转向其他产茶国；其三，以往的作坊式生产即使恢复，其产量也不足以应付日益扩大的国际市场的需求量。因此，国家要不惜代价恢复祁红的生产与出口，而且要在传统"作坊式"基础上，实施祁红的工业化生产。

于是，国家在安徽徽州与池州两地区筹建三个祁红工厂 —— 祁门茶厂、贵池茶厂和东至茶厂（原贵池茶厂尧渡分厂，于 1958 年独立）。祁门茶厂在 20 世纪 80 年代倒闭，而贵池茶厂和东至茶厂则合并为安徽国润茶业有限公司。

Beginning—the Era of Guichi Tea Factory (1950–1976)

创业伊始——贵池茶厂时代（1950–1976）

The Tunxi Branch of the China Tea Company (South Anhui Branch) constructed a new black tea factory. In 1952, Qimen Tea Factory, Guichi Tea Factory and Dongzhi Tea Factory were successively established. Qimen Tea Factory could be understood as a direct heir of the Hu Yuanlong brand, while Guichi Tea Factory and Dongzhi Tea Factory, both located in Chizhou, are direct heirs of the Yu Ganchen brand.

Regarding the process from the founding of Guichi Tea Factory in the early days of the People's Republic of China to its being restructured into 'Guorun Tea Industry Co., Ltd.' during the reform and opening-up, the old generation of workers in the early days of the factory still remembers vividly the difficulties in starting a business. They presented this historical picture to posterity by oral narration.

As an old revolutionary, the first party secretary of the factory was not proficient in business, but he was enthusiastic, open-minded and cherished technical talent. He fully supported the first factory director Xu Huaikun in carrying out his work, reviving Qimen Black Tea, which had disappeared since the outbreak of the war against Japanese Resistance in 1937. The

The old-timers of Guorun Tea Factory interviewed by the editorial board: Yang Huanzhang (first from the left) was a mechanical engineer and a model worker in Anhui Province, Yuan Tongchang (second from the left) was the director of the tea-making workshop in the 1950s, and Wang Yongkuan (third from the left) was the director of the tea-making workshop in the 1980s.

接受编委会采访的国润茶厂老前辈们．杨焕章（左一）为机械工程师、安徽省劳动模范．袁同昌（左二）为 20 世纪 50 年代制茶车间主任．汪永宽（左三）为 20 世纪 80 年代制茶车间主任。

nearly 100-year-old retiree still remembers when tea growers entered the factory to become tea makers. From tea farmers to tea makers, the subtle change in identity inspired professionalism and craftsmanship. It is especially unforgettable that when tea samples were sent from the tea garden to the tea maker, people had to cross mountains for one day and one night on a round trip.

The old told the young with one voice: Despite their lifetime devotion to making black tea for export, they had not developed the habit of drinking black tea. Why? Black tea is an export product for the country in for foreign trade. Although it is made by them, black tea is a national property. They cherish it, but have no right to enjoy it free of charge. Yuan Tongchang, a 92-year-old old worker of Guichi Tea Factory, recalled, "I started to work in Dongzhi in March 1950. Before that I was a tea grower. The initial conditions of Guichi Tea Factory were very tough. At that time, tea was collected by paying large amounts of cash to farmers. With no vehicles available, and bandits roaming in the mountains, people had to carry tea leaves on shoulders, escorted by armed forces. When tea plantation workers in the mountains came to the factory for a meeting, they had to climb mountains and ridges for one day and one night. When the factory was first established, the annual tea output was several thousand piculs, which rose steadily to 30,000 piculs in the 1990s." In the 1950s, as China's overall national strength was poor and weak, Guichi Tea Factory started from scratch with extremely limited capital investment. The factory building was still meticulously designed and constructed with high quality. The imported production equipment is of high quality and durable, leaving a precious industrial building heritage for future generations. Guichi Tea Factory lived up to the people's hopes and great trust. In April 1951, Guichi Tea Factory was put into operation, and its reputation in the domestic and foreign markets was soon restored. The quality of its producteven outshone that of its predecessors. Qimen black tea was rated as one of 'China's Top Ten Famous Teas' at the 1959 China's 'Top Ten Famous Tea' Appraisal Meeting along with Nanjing Yuhua Tea, Dongting Biluochun, Huangshan Maofeng, Lushan Yunwu

Tea, Liu'an Guapian, Junshan Yinzhen, Xinyang Maojian, Wuyi Yan Tea, Anxi Tieguanyin. By 1966, on the eve of the 'Cultural Revolution', when state leaders such as Mao Zedong, Zhou Enlai and Liu Shaoqi visited other countries, Qimen black tea was one of the necessary gifts accompanying them.

Today, strolling through the old factory area, people see that the old factory workshops can still produce exquisite handmade Qimen black tea products, and the old warehouse is still filled with tea fragrance. They all marvel at the complete functions of its production workshops and storage warehouse, amazed by the rich culture contained in Qimen black tea as seen from the inheritance of traditional techniques in the old production workshops.

中国茶业公司屯溪分公司（后称"皖南分公司"）是筹建新的红茶工厂的执行者。1952 年，祁门茶厂、贵池茶厂和东至茶厂相继成立。祁门茶厂可理解为胡元龙品牌的直系传承，而同在池州地区的贵池茶厂与东至茶厂则为余干臣氏品牌的嫡传。

The tea-making machine, which has been running for half a century, is maintained and repaired by tea factory workers all on their own

运行半个世纪之久的制茶机器完全由茶厂工人们自行维护修理。

有关中华人民共和国成立之初贵池茶厂建厂至改革开放更名"国润茶业有限公司"的历程，建厂初期的老一代对其创业艰难仍记忆犹新。他们用口述历史向后人展示了这段历史画卷。

首任厂党委书记作为一位老革命，虽并不精通业务，但热情、开明、爱惜技术人才，全力支持首任厂长徐怀琨开展工作，使得自 1937 年抗战爆发起即销声匿迹的祁红起死回生。现年近百岁的退休老人至今仍记得当初由茶叶种植农户进入工厂成为制茶工人的情景。从茶农到制茶工匠，身份的微妙变化，所激发出的是敬业精神与工匠精神，难忘当年自茶园送茶叶样品至制茶厂，往返需要翻山越岭步行一个昼夜。

老人们几乎异口同声地告诉后人：制作了一辈子的外销红茶，自己却至今没有养成喝红茶的习惯。为什么？红茶是为国家换取外汇的外销产品，尽管是自己亲手制成的，但那是国家财产，自己只有爱惜之情而无权无偿享用。现年 92 岁高龄的贵池茶厂老职工袁同昌老人回忆道"我 1950 年 3 月在东至参加工作，之前是种茶叶的茶农。初期的贵池茶厂条件很艰苦。当时收茶叶都是把大量现金付给农民。那时候没有汽车，山里还有土匪，需要人挑着担子武装押运。工作在山里的茶园人来厂开会，要翻山越岭，一天一夜。刚建厂时年产几千担茶，每年产量稳中有升，20 世纪 90 年代年产量达到 30 000 担。"20

Liang Qiushi (1903–1987) practiced the tradition of literati tea. When he came back from abroad, the first magazine he founded was Bitter Tea.

梁秋实（1903–1987）践行的是文人茶的传统，他留洋回来，办的第一份杂志即《苦茶》。

Liang Qiushi wrote a small autobiography in memory of his deceased wife, 'Recalling the Old Story of Huai Garden Dream - In Memoriam of my Wife, Ms. Cheng Jishu", in which he talked about tea many times. His wife, Ms. Cheng, was from Huizhou and versed in tea. She was also the first reader of Liang Qiushi's many translations of Shakespeare's works.

梁秋实写过纪念亡妻的小小自传《忆旧篇槐园梦忆 — 悼念故妻程季舒女士》，文中多处讲茶事。其妻程女士是徽州人，是懂茶之人，她也是梁秋实翻译莎士比亚许多稿子的第一读者。

Tea factory workers doing manual tea sifting.

茶厂工人在进行手工筛茶工序。

Honourary certificates won by
Guorun Qimen Black Tea and the
social events in which it has been
involved (photos) in recent years

近年国润祁红所赢得的荣誉证
书及参与的社会活动（组照）。

世纪 50 年代在我国整体国力积贫积弱的大背景下，贵
池茶厂以极其有限的资金投入白手起家，所建厂房仍是
精心设计的、高质量施工的，所进口生产设备质量上乘、
经久耐用，为后人留下了一份珍贵的工业建筑遗产。当
年的贵池茶厂没有辜负人民的希望与重托。1951 年 4 月，
贵池茶厂正常投产，很快在国内外市场上重现当年风采，
其产品质量甚至是青出于蓝的。祁红于 1959 年中国"十
大名茶"评比会上与南京雨花茶、洞庭碧螺春、黄山毛峰、
庐山云雾茶、六安瓜片、君山银针、信阳毛尖、武夷岩茶、
安溪铁观音等并列为"中国十大名茶"。至 1966 年"文革"
前夕，毛泽东、周恩来、刘少奇等国家领导人出国访问，
祁红都是随行必备的礼品之一。

今天，当人们漫步老厂区，看到老厂房仍可出产手工祁
红精品，老库房仍弥漫着茶香，无不赞叹其生产车间、
储物仓库之功能完备，而老生产车间的传统工艺之承袭，
更令人感叹祁红所蕴含的文化之丰厚。

Operation and Transformation:
The Era of Guorun Tea Industry (1977–)

守业与转型—国润茶业时代（1977–）

As a large-scale tea-making enterprise with a glorious history, Guorun Tea Industry Co., Ltd. has been developing rapidly. Its products have changed from being oriented just for export to integration of domestic and international sales, from export supply and OEM production to a business model of 'original brands as dominant and OEM supply as auxiliary'; from simple acquisition and processing to integration of tea garden management, initial production, acquisition and processing, research and development, and innovation. Sticking to its own

From the structural column on the outer wall of the manual sorting factory, it can be seen that the original one-story building has been expanded for the development of the tea factory.

从手工拣厂外壁的结构柱上可以看出，原本一层的平房因茶厂发展需要而进行了加建。

development path, Guichi Tea Factory has earned its triumphant return, and also dozens of honours, mainly as follows:

- In 1983, Qimen Black Tea won a Gold Medal of the National Light Industry Quality Products Appraisal Committee.
- In April 1986, Anhui Provincial People's Government awarded Guichi Tea Factory the title of 'Key Export Production Enterprise of Anhui Province.'
- In September 1987, Qimen black tea won a gold medal of the 26th World Food Congress in Brussels.
- In April 2001, Runsi Qimen black tea produced by Guichi Tea Factory won the gold medal at the first China (Wuhu) International Tea Expo.
- In June 2003, Anhui Provincial Tea Company's Guichi Tea Factory (state-owned) was transformed into a joint-stock company of Anhui Guorun Tea Co., Ltd.
- In October 2005, Runsi Qimen black tea won the gold medal at the first China International Tea Expo.
- In 2009, Runsi Qimen Black Tea was rated as one of the 'Top Ten Famous Tea Brands of China World Expo' in the 2010 Shanghai World Expo and was designated as the special tea for the United Nations Pavilion. At the World Expo, then Vice President Xi Jinping visited the site to taste Runsi Qimen Black Tea. UN Secretary-General Ban Ki-moon, Finnish President Halonen, Thai Princess Sirindhorn and other state leaders all spoke highly of Runsi Qimen Black Tea.
- In 2012, the 'Runsi' trademark was recognized as 'China's Famous Trademark' by the State Administration for Industry and Commerce.
- In June 2015, Runsi Qimen Black Tea won a special gold medal for black tea again at the Beijing International Tea Industry Exhibition.
- In 2016, 'Runsi Black Tea' was recognized by the State General Administration of Quality Supervision, Inspection and Quarantine as 'PDO Ecological Products of the People's Republic of China'.

Compared with these elderly people, the current chairman,
Mr Yin Tianji, is a member of the 'new generation starting
to work in the 1980s'. He started to work in the factory as a
technician upon graduating from university after the 'Cultural
Revolution' and has also been unconditionally dedicated to the
tea factory. He recalled the past to his friends:

"From 1994, VAT reform posed a big challenge for enterprise.
The rise of the domestic green tea market certainly had an
impact on the black tea market in China … The European
Union issued high import standards, posing a major test for
China's tea exports, as their standards were 100 times higher
than the domestic standards. At that time, China's black
tea was mainly exported to the European Union, and many
manufacturers faced severe tests that year. After 2000, Qimen
Black Tea manufacturers faced even more difficulties. Therefore,
Guichi Tea Factory had to make reforms. Fortunately, Guorun
has been sailing along the maritime Silk Road into Europe."

" … With regard to the Laomaocha Warehouse, for
example, its walls, floors and roofs are everywhere infused
with the tea fragrance of decades. Its achievements are the
result of hard work of several generations, and we should
not let it disappear in the hands of our generation!"

"I was able to return to this factory, in fact, at that time, firstly
because I had the courage and then I had to be confident. At
that time, many colleagues in the city were making green tea,
thinking that black tea did not earn money. I thought they
lacked understanding of Qimen black tea. I know Qimen black
tea's influence abroad and see its potential value. I believe that
the world's three largest high-quality scented teas cannot be
buried all the time. To destroy such a good brand in our hands
is a crime! I accepted the bank's debt, an action extremely rare
under the trend of restructuring at that time; but this also
planted a seed of good faith, enabling us to enter a healthy

After being included in the second batch
of China's 20th century architectural
heritage list, a special guideboard has
been made for the factory area

入选第二批中国 20 世纪建筑遗产
名录后，厂区制作了带有标识性的
导视牌

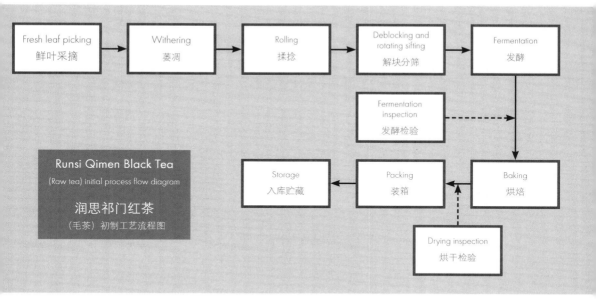

| Fresh leaf picking 鲜叶采摘 | Withering 萎凋 | Rolling 揉捻 | Deblocking and rotating sifting 解块分筛 | Fermentation 发酵 |

Fermentation inspection 发酵检验

Runsi Qimen Black Tea
(Raw tea) initial process flow diagram
润思祁门红茶
(毛茶) 初制工艺流程图

| Storage 入库贮藏 | Packing 装箱 | Baking 烘焙 |

Drying inspection 烘干检验

operation. I believe Guorun Qimen Black Tea is excellent and that we must be public-spirited. Before the restructuring, most Qimen black tea enterprises depended on export. We started to use the Runsi brand as a domestic brand, not limited to export, and thus became more resilient to market changes. In 2003, the state-owned Guichi Tea Factory was renamed 'Guorun Tea Co., Ltd.' It is actually a limited liability company controlled by the private sector. We are not a beneficiary of vested interest in restructuring, but are committed to the revitalization and development of Qimen black tea. We share weal and woe with all employees. This is our self-discipline."

"Fortunately, after restructuring, some of our technical advisers in teamaking have stayed. These people are a rare treasure. Another good thing is the preservation of the old factory buildings. Our intuition has told us that the original buildings should be kept, and that we should repair old buildings as they were in the past. At that time, the management habits of staff from the old state-owned enterprises were still good.

The good habits of machine maintenance and plant cleaning have inadvertently prolonged the life of the old buildings and equipment. Our perception is: first of all, the old Qimen black tea factory and technology have been preserved; secondly, we have realized restructuring, kept export sales and transited domestic sales. In the Qimen black tea industry, our factory is the first to start domestic sales by introducing our brand. Our appearance at the Shanghai World Expo in 2010 has awakened the Qimen black tea's factory area and inspired the spirit of Qimen black tea."

"In 2017, we were added to China's 20th century architectural heritage list. This shows that Qimen Black Tea, as a special symbol, is irreplaceable."

作为一家有着光荣历史的大型制茶企业，国润茶业有限公司在这个阶段得到飞跃式的发展。其产品生产由单纯出口转向内外销一体化；由出口供货、贴牌生产转向"以自有品牌为主导，贴牌供货为辅助"的经营模式；由单纯的收购加工转向集茶园管理、初制生产、收购加工、

One corner of the Runsi Qimen Black Tea Garden.

润思祁红茶园一隅。

研发创新为一体。贵池茶厂坚守阵地的局面，在为自己赢得了华丽转身的契机时，荣誉也数以十计，主要是：

Tea garden workers picking fresh leaves.

茶园工人在采摘鲜叶。

- 1983 年，祁红获得全国轻工业优质产品评比会金质奖章。
- 1986 年 4 月，安徽省人民政府授予贵池茶厂"安徽省出口生产重点企业"称号。
- 1987 年 9 月，祁红荣获布鲁塞尔第 26 届世界优质食品会金质奖章。
- 2001 年 4 月，贵池茶厂所出品的润思品牌祁门红茶荣获首届中国（芜湖）国际茶业博览会金质奖。
- 2003 年 6 月，安徽省茶叶公司贵池茶厂（国有性质）整体改制为股份制的安徽国润茶业有限公司。
- 2005 年 10 月，润思祁门红茶荣获首届中国国际茶业博览会金质奖。
- 2009 年，润思祁红入选 2010 年上海世博会"中国世博十大名茶"，并被指定为联合国馆专用茶。在此次世博会上，时任国家副主席的习近平同志亲临现场品赏润思祁红，联合国秘书长潘基文、芬兰总统哈洛宁、泰国公主诗琳通等多国政要都对润思祁红予以高度评价。
- 2012 年"润思商标被国家工商总局认定为中国驰名商标"。
- 2015 年 6 月，润思牌祁红再次夺得北京国际茶业展红茶特别金奖。
- 2016 年"润思红茶"被国家质检总局认定为"中华人民共和国生态原产地保护产品"。

相比这些耄耋老者，现任董事长殷天霁先生是"文革"结束后大学毕业来厂任技术员的"80 年代新一辈"，同样对茶厂倾注了无条件的爱。他向友人回忆那段往事：

"从 1994 年开始，因为增值税改革，对企业来说是大的挑战，从国内来说国内绿茶市场兴起，对红茶市场有一定冲击 …… 欧盟出台了高标准的进口标准，对中国茶叶出口是重大考验，其标准比国内标准高百倍。当时中国红茶主要出口欧盟，那一年很多厂家面临严峻考验，2000 年以后，祁红厂家雪上加霜，更加艰难。为此，贵池茶厂必须做出改革。幸运的是，国润一直航行在入欧的海上丝绸之路中。"

"……仅以老毛茶仓库为例，它的四壁、地板与屋顶无处不浸满了几十年茶香，积淀着几代人的辛勤劳作，不能忍心在我们这一代人手中消失！"

"我能够回到这个厂子里，其实当时首先是有勇气，其次要有自信。当时市里同行很多做绿茶，说红茶赚不到钱，我认为他们对祁红缺乏了解，我知道祁红在国外的影响力，要看到它的潜在价值。我相信，世界三大高香茶不可能一直被埋没，这么好的东西在我们手上毁掉了，就是犯罪！我承接下了银行的债务，这在当时改制的风潮下是极其罕见的，但这也种下了一颗诚信的种子，使我们进入良性运转；相信国润祁红一定是好的，要有公心；在改制之前，大部分的祁红企业依赖于出口外贸，我们开始用润思品牌做国内品牌，不局限于出口，市场变动承受能力变强；2003年改制，国营贵池茶厂改称为"国润茶业有限公司"，其实是民营控股的有限责任公司。我们不是作为改制的既得利益者，而是致力于祁红的振兴和发展，是与全体职工同甘共苦，这是我们的自律。"

"比较荣幸的是，改制过后我们的一些制茶方面的技术顾问都留了下来。这些人是难得的财富。再有对老厂房的保护，我们直觉就应该保持原貌，也就是修旧如旧。那时候从老国企过来的职工管理习惯还是好的，机器保养、厂房清理，好的习惯无意中延长了老建筑、老设备的寿命。我们的感悟是：首先，老的祁红厂和工艺保留下来了；其次，我们实现了转型，坚持外销，并转型内销。在祁红行业，我厂是第一个以品牌导入做内销的。2010年我们亮相上海世博会，唤醒了祁红厂区，振奋了祁红精神。"

"2017年我们又入选了中国20世纪建筑遗产名录，这说明祁红作为特殊的符号，是无可替代的。"

How Runsi Qimen Black Tea Manages to Keep up With the Times

润思祁红何以历久弥新

Choice materials. The raw tea leaves for the Qimen black tea products of Runsi series come from the golden tea-producing areas in Mount Huang and Mount Jiuhua, which are located between 29–30 north latitude and 117–118 east longitude. This is a mountainous region. Areas suitable for tea tree growth and producing high-quality tea are slopes with an elevation of about 600m. The annual average rainfall is 1,650–2,000 mm. The soil quality is red-yellow soil with high gravel content, good water permeability and high fertility. After decades of investigation and sifting, three tea planting bases have been established successively, namely Tongchun Tea Garden, Huangshan Wushi Tea Garden and Gu Xi Tea Garden. In 1984, the National Tea Tree Improved Variety Approval Committee approved Castanopsis eyrei leaf species in the Qimen Black Tea Planting Base as a 'National Improved Variety of Tea Trees'.

Unique processing techniques. The production processes of Runsi Qimen black tea are classified into crude processes and refining processes.

The refining process of Runsi Qimen Black Tea is complex and fine. Generally, it is carried out by single-stage charging and multi-stage recovery. After being dried by the raw fire, the raw tea is taken out by the multi-barrel loading machine, and then the raw tea is processed by four-line single machines, namely, self-line, long-length line, round-tea line and light-tea line. Tea at each head and tail of each line is treated separately. The whole operation process roughly consists of more than ten procedures such as charging tea leaves for processing, drying with first firing, segmentation and reclaiming (raw sifting, shaking sifting, and punching), sifting (garden sifting, tight-door sifting, and final

On the sieve mesh frame for manual tea sifting, the traces of handwriting, reading 'directly under China Tea Guichi' and 'April 1953 AD' were faintly visible.

手工筛萃的筛网架上,"中茶贵池直属公元一九五三年四月"的字迹隐约可见。

rotating sifting), winnowing, trimming (machine trimming, color sorting), complement of fire by clear breeze, blending and even stacking, and packing of finished products.

This refining stage following the making of black crude tea naturally has more refined and rigorous requirements on technology than the previous stage. First of all, the raw tea of different lengths, thicknesses and weight should be sieved, cut, and rolled to dress the appearance, and then winnowed and trimmed to remove impurities to make mesh hole-sized tea semi-finished products with uniform tenderness, neat length and consistent size. Finally, according to the quality requirements of commercial tea, many mesh hole-sized tea products should be spliced and piled evenly according to a certain proportion to become finished tea products. At the same time, in order to improve dryness, maintain quality, and facilitate storage and volatilization of tea aroma, drying treatment such as firing should be carried out. Finally, Runsi Qimen black tea products with excellent shape and quality are developed after they have passed packing review and inspection.

After two processes of primary production and refining, a variety of black tea products suitable for different consumer groups are produced. The best products can be used as 'national gifts', while general products produced by the round-tea line and so on are cheap and fine products for daily consumption by the public.

Runsi Qimen Black Tea rated as one of the 'Top Ten Famous Teas in China World Expo'.

润思祁门红茶入选"中国世博十大名茶"。

选料精良。润思系列产品的祁红，原材料的茶叶出自地处北纬 29°~30°、东经 117°~118° 之间的黄山、九华山一带的黄金产茶区。此地为山地，适宜茶树生长并出品优质茶叶的地带为海拔 600 m 左右的坡地，年平均降雨量为 1 650 – 2 000 mm，土质为石砾含量、透水透气程度均良好且肥力较高的红黄壤。经过几十年的考察和筛选，先后建立了同春茶园、黄山乌石茶园和古溪茶园等三个茶叶种植基地。1984 年，全国茶树良种审定委员会审定祁红种植基地的槠叶种为"全国茶树良种"。

独特的加工工艺。润思祁门红茶生产工艺分为粗制工艺和精制工艺两种。

润思祁门红茶的精制工艺，复杂而精细。一般采用单级付制、多级收回的方式进行，毛茶付制毛火烘干后，用联装作业机取料，然后按照本身路、长身路、圆身路、轻身路四路单机制作。各路头尾茶单独处理。整个作业流程大致包括投料付制、毛火烘干、切分取料（毛筛、抖筛、切轧）、筛分（园筛、紧门、撩筛）、风选、拣剔（机拣、色选）、清风补火、拼和匀堆、成品装箱等十多道工序。

这个红毛茶制成后的精制阶段，在工艺上要求自然又比前一阶段更为精细严苛。首先，要将长短粗细、轻重曲直不一的毛茶经过筛分、切轧取料后整饰外形，风选、拣剔后去除杂质，制成嫩度均匀、长短整齐、大小一致的孔号茶半成品，最后按照商品茶的品质要求，将众多孔号茶按照一定比例进行拼和匀堆，成为成品茶。同时为了提高干度，保持品质，便于贮藏和挥发茶香，还要进行补火等烘干处理，最后，通过装箱审评检验后，才成为形质兼优的润思祁门红茶商品。

经过初制、精制两个工艺加工流程，即产生出多种多样的适应不同消费群体的红茶系列产品。其最上等的精品，可作"国礼"，而由圆身路等产生出的一般性产品，则是价廉物美的大众日常消费产品。

Runsi Qimen Black Tea was tasted by guests in the 'World Harmony Tea Party'

润思祁红在"世界和谐茶会"活动中接受来宾品鉴。

Experts were tasting Qimen black tea in the display room on one side of the sorting factory.

专家在拣厂一侧的展示室中品鉴祁红茶。

The Diversified and Integrated Development Strategy of "Guorun Qimen Black Tea"

多元一体的"国润祁红"的发展策略

1. The spread of the fitness function of black tea
健体功能的作用传播

According to traditional Chinese medicine, Qimen black tea is sweet and warm, which can nourish the body's *yang* energy, generate heat and warm the stomach. The folk have long regarded Qimen black tea as a good medicine to warm the stomach and help digestion. In Guichi Tea Factory-Guorun Tea Industry Company, although most of the old employees have no habit of drinking black tea, when anyone suffers from dyspepsia, Qimen black tea will be used as a medical prescription by the factory clinic. At the same time, they constantly invite professional teams on food nutrition and medicine from home and abroad to conduct rigorous inspection and analysis on all Runsi products.

As early as 1995, through contacts with international organizations, a study on 'Qimen Black Tea's Effect on Human Health' was carried out in the United Kingdom, the United States, Canada and other countries. Research reports overseas have pointed out that although Qimen black tea's curative effect cannot restore a patient's blood circulation to normal, it is helpful to improve the unblocked condition of blood vessels. Oxidized condensates such as theaflavin and thearubigins in Qimen black tea have antioxidant and anti-free radical effects. Tea polyphenol compounds in Qimen black tea can reduce cholesterol in blood pressure and obviously improve the ratio of high density protein to low density fatty white cells in blood. Caffeine in Qimen black tea can relax blood vessels, accelerate respiration and reduce

blood lipids. Qimen black tea contains not only a variety of
water-soluble vitamins, but also microelement potassium.
After brewing, 70% of potassium can be dissolved in tea water
to enhance cardiac blood circulation and reduce calcium
consumption in the body. Therefore, Qimen black tea is
effective in preventing and treating apoplexy, heart disease and
cerebrovascular disease. The report cautiously concludes that
for people who drink 5 cups of black tea a day, the vascular
stretch of heart disease patients can be increased from 6% to
10%, while that of ordinary people can be increased by about
13%. Their risk of stroke is 69% lower than those who do not
drink black tea.

In October 2017, Yuan Tongchang, the
92-year-old director of the old tea-making
workshop, returned to the inspection
building to demonstrate the manual tea
inspection methods in the past.

2017 年 10 月，92 岁的老制茶车间主
任袁同昌回到检验楼中，为大家演示
当年的手工验茶的方法。

传统中医认为：祁红甘温，可养人体阳气、生热暖胃。
而民间早已将祁红作为暖胃助消化的良药。在贵池茶
厂 — 国润茶业的老职工中，尽管大多没有饮红茶的习
惯，但身体出现消化不良状况时，厂医务室会将祁红
作为医疗处方。同时他们不断邀请中外食品营养学、
医药学的专业团队对所有润思系列产品作严苛的检验
分析。

早在 1995 年，经与国际机构联络，在英、美、加拿大
等国开展了"祁红对人体健康的作用"的研究。国外有研
究报告指出：祁红的疗效虽然无法使病人的血液流通恢
复正常，但有助于改善血管畅通状况。祁红中的茶黄素
和茶红素等氧化缩合物具有抗氧化、抗自由基的作用；
祁红中的茶多酚类化合物可以降低血压中的胆固醇，明
显改善血液中高密度蛋白与低密度脂肪白的比值；祁红
中的咖啡碱能舒张血管、加快呼吸、降低血脂；祁红除
含多种水溶性维生素外，还富含微量元素钾，经冲泡，
70% 的钾可溶于茶水中，增强心脏血液循环，并能减少
钙在体内的消耗。因此，祁红对防治中风、心脏病和脑
血管病等是具有相当的功效的。此报告谨慎做出结论：
每天喝 5 杯红茶的人，心脏病患者血管舒展度可以 6%
增加至 10%，而常人的血管舒展度能增加到 13% 左右；
脑中风的发病危险比不喝红茶的人低 69%。

2. Qimen black tea culture should be spread
祁红文化应传播

China has a long history of tea. The great
variety of teas in China can be classified into
traditional famous teas and historical famous
teas. Therefore, many versions of China's 'Top
Ten Famous Tea' have emerged.

In the Panama World Expo 1915,
Biluochun, Qimen Black Tea was rated as
one of the Top Ten Famous Teas in China,
the other nine being Xinyang Maojian, West
Lake Longjing, Junshan Yinzhen, Huangshan
Maofeng, Wuyi Yancha, Duyun Maojian,
Tieguanyin and Liu'an Guapian.

Tea workers picking tea in the factory.

茶工们拣厂中拣茶。

In 1959, China's 'Top Ten Famous Tea' Appraisal
Committee listed Nanjing Yuhua Tea, Dongting Biluochun,
Huangshan Maofeng, Lushan Yunwu Tea, Liu'an Guapian,
Junshan Yinzhen, Xinyang Maojian, Wuyi Yancha, Anxi
Tieguanyin and Qimen Black Tea as the Top Ten Famous Teas
in China.

In 2002, Hong Kong *Wen Wei Po* listed West Lake
Longjing, Jiangsu Biluochun, Anhui Maofeng, Hunan Junshan
Yinzhen, Xinyang Maojian, Anhui Qimen Black Tea, Anhui
Guapian, Duyun Maojian, Wuyi Yancha, Fujian Tieguanyin as
the Top Ten Famous Teas in China.

In 2009, Qimen Black Tea was rated as one of the 'Top
Ten Famous Teas of China World Expo' in the 2010 Shanghai
World Expo.

中国茶叶历史悠久、种类繁多，有传统名茶和历史名茶
之分，所以中国的"十大名茶"在过去也有多种说法。

1915 年巴拿马万国博览会将碧螺春、信阳毛尖、西湖龙井、
君山银针、黄山毛峰、武夷岩茶、祁门红茶、都匀毛尖、
铁观音、六安瓜片列为中国十大名茶。

1959 年中国十大名茶评比会将南京雨花茶、洞庭碧螺春、黄山毛峰、庐山云雾茶、六安瓜片、君山银针、信阳毛尖、武夷岩茶、安溪铁观音、祁门红茶列为中国十大名茶。

2002 年《香港文汇报》将西湖龙井、江苏碧螺春、安徽毛峰、湖南君山银针、信阳毛尖、安徽祁门红、安徽瓜片、都匀毛尖、武夷岩茶、福建铁观音列为中国十大名茶。

2009 年，祁红入选 2010 年上海世博会中国世博十大名茶"。

3. Runsi Qimen Black Tea is a 'new business card' of cultural Chizhou
润思祁红是文化池州"新名片"

Sharing the stories of Qimen Black Tea is the goal of properly making it the 'business card' of cultural Chizhou. In history, Homer's Epics in the West and the *Records of the Grand Historian* in China can be passed on to this day, because in these works stories are used to transmit all aspects of culture. If the vivid culture of tea is incorporated into stories, tea drinkers will never get tired of hearing them. Tea stories in cultural Chizhou have very rich contents, such as tea and health preservation, tea and beauty, tea and history, tea and etiquette, tea and celebrities at home and abroad, tea and architectural culture, tea and art music, tea and the 'decoding' of cultural development. Tea's flavour is beautiful because she embodies everything deeply; tea fragrance is beautiful because of the unforgettable fragrant aftertaste.

It is a formidable task to fully epitomize, in the construction of cultural Chizhou, the high aroma, high status and high quality of the tea produced by Qimen Black Tea Factory, which has been listed as one of China's 20th-century architectural heritages. Then to express the refreshing elegance of Qimen black tea and its amazing historical influence on the present, we should start with a research on the disappearance

of the old factory area of Qimen Tea Factory, a fact that even
the neighboring Guorun Tea Industry Company bemoans. The
discovery of the old factory area is also an exploration of the
Qimen black tea culture connecting the past and the present,
China and the world; Runsi Qimen Black Tea is a cultural
product with life and soul, while the old factory building
located in Chizhou City and the old teahouse on Yaodu Street
in Dongzhi County are the sources of Runsi Qimen Black Tea,
which must be treasured. Tasting Runsi Qimen black tea can
make the public think of an old factory building that has been
in operation for nearly 70 years. What a nostalgic story it is!

Therefore, from the perspective of developing China's black
tea culture for the world, why can't we imagine having a World
Union of Black Tea Museums sponsored by China? Why can't
we carry forward and develop Qimen black tea in China via 'the
Belt and Road'? Why can't the world's attention be retrieved
for China's Qimen black tea? We are well-placed to proclaim
that everyone will be enchanted by Qimen black tea's heartfelt
mellow fragrance.

讲好祁红故事，是做好文化池州"名片"的目标。历史上
西方的《荷马史诗》或中国的《史记》能够传承至今，
就是用故事承载了文化的方方面面。将生动的"茶"文化
融进故事中，会让品茶者百听不厌。从文化池州的"茶"
故事看，可讲的内容很丰富，如茶与养生、茶与美容、
茶与历史、茶与礼仪、茶与中外古今名流、茶与建筑文化、
茶与美术音乐、茶与文化发展的解码等。茶韵之所以美好，
是因为她深藏着一切；茶香之所以美好，是因为香茶回
味难忘。

将已入选中国 20 世纪建筑遗产名录的祁红茶厂所产茶
之高香、高贵、高品质的特质，尽情表现在文化池州建
设上是一项艰巨的任务。那么祁红的清新典雅、从历史
走来的风范感染今人的妙绝，就需要我们从找寻祁门茶
厂老厂区的消失，即令毗邻的国润茶业也为之扼腕惋惜
的历程入手。发现老厂区，也是发掘联系中外古今的祁

红文化：润思祁红是有生命有灵魂的文化产品，而地处池州市的老厂房与东至县尧渡街老茶号等，就是饮水思源的润思祁红之源头，必须加以珍惜。品润思祁红能令公众联想到一家沿袭近 70 年却仍在运作的老厂房，是怎样写意的"乡愁"故事。

由此，从发展中国、面向世界的红茶文化入手，为什么我们不能设想拥有中国倡导主持的世界红茶博物馆联盟？为什么我们不能借"一带一路"走好中国祁红的传承与发展之路？为什么不能找回中国的祁红令世界瞩目的目光？我们有理由说：祁红那由心底释放出的醇香，会让每位品到的人皆为之陶醉并喜爱上它。

Tea samples and inspection tools in the
inspection building.

检验楼中的茶叶样本和检验工具。

Postscript

Guorun Keemun Delivers Miracles

编后

"国润祁红"是发生并创造"奇迹"之地

ON MARCH 15, 2018, A SEMINAR ON *The Research Report on the Creative Design of Anhui Guorun Tea Industrial Co., Ltd.* co-hosted by the 20th Century Architectural Heritage Committee of China Cultural Relics Academy and Chizhou Municipal People's Government was held at the Hall of Embodied Treasures of the Palace Museum, a place inscribed into the second list of China's 20th century architectural heritage. As indicated by Shan Jixiang, Director of the Palace Museum, the seminar demonstrates the connotations and essence of the tangible and intangible cultural heritage about Keemun through the research and promotion of excellent cases of China's 20th century architectural heritage projects. Mayor Yong Chenghan of Chizhou praised the keen insight of the experts on Chinese cultural relics and museums who have discovered Guorun Keemun Old Factory, and expressed the hope that it would be brought to life to the benefit of local people and it would contribute to making Chinese tea go global.

On May 19, 2018, China Cultural Relics Academy held its annual academic conference in Quanzhou and held the exhibition of China's 20th Architectural Heritage List at the Weiyuanlou Square in Quanzhou, where Guorun Keemun Old Factory stood side by side with the Shougang with a history of over 100 years for industrial production. Such a design highlighted the cultural dimension of Guorun Keemun heritage and attracted numerous people to stop for a look. On May 20, 2018, at the Seminar on the People and Events Related to New China's 20th Century Architectural Heritage held by Quanzhou Maritime Transportation Museum (designed by late architect Yong Hongxun), the author spoke on 'New China's 20th Century Architectural Heritage as the New Blue Sea in Urgent Need of Protection and Utilization: Respect for the People and Retrospect of the Things Related to Architectural Heritage', illustrating the reasons why the Guorun Keemun Factory has been recognized as China's 20th Century Architectural Heritage.

China's tea culture dating back to a long time ago hinges on the role of the men of letters whose aesthetics of life plays a decisive part in tea culture. An object is never too beautiful, an article is never too delicate, and an act is never too meticulous. I'm deeply interested in the architecture for Keemun production because I was attracted by its exceptional cultural charm at the first sight of it. At the recommendation of Xiu Long, Director-General of the China Cultural Relics Academy, I visited Chizhou for the first time between August 24 and 26, 2017, and I discovered and came to love the Guorun Keemun Old Factory together with my fellow colleagues. I would like to share three points about the visit.

Firstly, it was for discovery and identification. When I first walked into the Guorun Keemun Factory on August 24, 2017, I felt the living industrial remains which are simple but appealing, and associated it with the criteria for selecting China's 20th architectural heritage, appreciated its inheritance, and felt the confidence of the Factory Head Yin Tianji who told us moving stories about the Keemun factory. Under the support of Chizhou Municipal People's Government, the investigation, interview, photography and research centering on the Factory began in early October 2017.

Secondly, it was for discovery and evaluation. In early October 2017, the expert team of the 20th Century Architectural Heritage Committee of China Cultural Relics Academy did not simply aim for inscribing the Guorun Keemun Old Factory into the Second List of China's 20th Architectural Heritage Projects. More importantly, they wished to make the inscription drive the rapid development of the cultural programs in Chizhou. For one thing, they must elaborate how the architecture of Guorun Keemun Factory reflected the architectural style in the beginning days of New China, and how the tea factory, far from impressive in terms of both acreage and output, became a special example of China's 20th century architectural heritage. For another, the Keemun black

In August 2017 the expert team followed Director-general Xiu Long to visit Guorun Keemun.

2017 年 8 月，专家团队随修龙理事长首次造访国润祁红。

tea famous around the world shall be connected with the 'Belt and Road' Initiative being pursued in China to create the style, sentiment, mentality and lifestyle related to Keemun as part of its social and cultural value. Gladstone, a four-time British Prime Minister, once said, "If you are cold, tea will warm you; if you are too heated, it will cool you; If you are depressed, it will cheer you; If you are excited, it will calm you."

Thirdly, it was for design inspection and Keemun brand dissemination. After Chizhou Municipal People's Government put forward the 12-Point Creative Design Planning for Guorun Keemun Guichi Old Tea Factory in January 2018, we invited design masters and famous experts on planning, architecture, cultural relics and museums to inspect Guorun Keemun from March 3 to 5, 2018, the aim of which was to prepare for the seminar to be held in the Hall of Embodied Treasures of the Palace Museum.

To disseminate the stories about Keemun, we headed for Chizhou Keemun Factory in late April 2018 to discuss matters

A group photo of the inspection team at the Guorun Keemun
Old Factory in March 2018

2018 年 3 月，考察组在国润祁红老茶厂合影。

about Guorun Keemun together with the leaders of the Municipal Culture, Radio and Information Bureau and the Municipal Planning Bureau of Chizhou City. While standing in the Xiaokeng Tea Farm, we see good tea only grows in a well-protected environment, and by associating Zen with tea can we reach a realm of the tea Zen. This book tells tales about the past and the quality of Guorun Keemun. All in all, a few events deserve special mention.

It is reported that at 17:00 on October 20, 2015, the Chinese President and his wife arrived at Clarence House to enjoy English-style afternoon tea with Prince Charles, which usually used the tea processed from Keemun black tea. For Chinese people, be it the most essential seven necessities for a home, like fuel, rice, oil, salt, soy sauce, vinegar and tea, or the *qin*, chess, calligraphy, painting, poetry, wine and tea essential for scholarship, Chinese culture and life are inseparable from tea. The British mostly drink black tea, while the

afternoon tea represents their own culture. On October 20, 2015, Xi Jinping spoke at the state banquet in the Buckingham Palace; "China's tea has added a lot of interest to the life of the British, who have ingeniously made it into English-style black tea. The communication and mutual learning between China and Britain has made huge contributions to human progress." The Keemun tale told by President Xi in Britain manifests that Keemun black tea has good reason to contribute to the wonderful landscape of China and of the world at large.

To inscribe Guorun Keemun Old Factory into China's 20th Century Architectural Heritage List and to understand the moving stories related to the tea-making people and events in Chizhou, the expert team from the editorial department for *China's Architectural Heritage* visited Guichi Factory in Chizhou eight times, with a view of opening up a new chapter for Keemun's tales while looking back on its past. The display platform marked with the guiding logo 'Guorun Keemun' in the Guichi Factory shows that the dissemination of Keemun black tea has been put onto the agenda. As early as early 2017, Chinese Foreign Minister Wang Yi, after a sip of the tea, commented it was the "noblest queen", a publicity slogan that could not be more apt! Today the Keemun black tea brings even more diversified life experiences, like travelling on the tea road dating back thousands of years, living in the guesthouse of the tea farmer, enjoying tea-flavoured food, relishing the taste of tea, listening to tea tales, talking about tea culture, and appreciating the Zen associated with tea, which are all intended to bring health and happiness with tea.

I would like to say that it is the commitment and perseverance of the Factory Head Yin that has impressed me most though the exquisite making of the Guorun Keemun Old Factory; itis amazing indeed. To speak from the perspective of the four decades of reform and opening-up, what Guichi Factory has left behind is the rapid pace of opening-up, and the development course of the perseverance of the people of Guorun Keemun; to speak from the perspective of the 70 years since the founding of the People's Republic of China, what remains in the old houses is about the inheritance of architecture, handicraft and articles, representing a set of gorgeous photos of China's industrial culture. After the photographers returned from the warehouse with its aroma of tea, we see from the reddish photos the color of Keemun black tea and understand why the Factory Head Yin declined all developers and waited for the day of cultural construction of Chizhou, home to hundreds of thousands of tea farmers and workers who are deeply attached to the land. It reflects the whole nation's respect for and consciousness of the charming Chinese tea culture.

Why has Guorun Keemun become what it is, and how does it keep delivering miracles? Does it just bring people teachers, soulmates and friends? Or is it because the current use of Guichi Old Factory reflects memories of the past and has contemporary implications? Actually, as we now need to do a good job in both heritage inheritance and generating creativity, the Keemun miracle is to set new benchmarks in its legacy, to glorify Chinese tea culture, and to associate Keemun with oriental culture as well as the world of culture.

I believe here will emerge the 'Keemun' new brand, which will enjoy huge popularity in China and the world at large. Under the influence of the 'Belt and Road' Initiative, the area is bound to become a park for the world tea expo that gathers the world's three high aroma teas. There is logic behind the development of Guorun Keemun in Chizhou and good reason for its success. All these constitute the impetus for our team to study, appreciate and disseminate it.

2018 年 3 月 15 日，在第二批中国 20 世纪建筑遗产地 —— 故宫宝蕴楼 —— 召开 "安徽国润茶业有限公司创意设计调研报告" 研讨会，该会议由中国文物学会 20 世纪建筑遗产委员会与池州市人民政府合办举行。恰如单霁翔院长所说，其成果针对中国 20 世纪建筑遗产项目优秀个案的研究与推广会，它用祁红全遗产向世人展示物质与非物质兼得一身的内涵与精髓。池州市雍成瀚市长在赞赏国润祁红老厂房被中国文博建筑专家发现的独到慧眼时，希望通过专家建言使它 "活起来"，造福池州人民，也为中华茶文化走向世界有所贡献。

2018 年 5 月 19 日，中国建筑学会在泉州举办 2018 年学术年会，特在泉州威远楼广场举办 "中国 20 世纪建筑遗产名录展"，国润祁红旧厂房与有百年历史的中国工业遗产首都钢铁公司并列呈现，表现了国润祁红遗产的文化特质，吸引了数以万计市民驻足的目光。2018 年 5 月 20 日，在泉州海上交通博物馆（已故建筑学家杨洪勋设计）举办的"新中国 20 世纪建筑遗产的人和事学术研讨会"上，笔者做了《中国 20 世纪建筑遗产是亟待保护利用的新蓝海 —— 关于建筑遗产事件与人的敬畏与回望》发言，讲述了国润祁红厂入选中国 20 世纪建筑遗产的理由。

中国茶文化的源远流长取决于文人的参与，其生活美学对茶文化的作用是决定性的。器往往不嫌其美，物往往不厌其精，行往往不讳其细。现在思考，本人之所以沉溺于祁红茶的生产场景建筑中，有以心逐物之感，是因为从一开始便体味到它不平凡的文化内涵。我是在中国建筑学会理事长修龙引导下，于 2017 年 8 月 24 日 —8 月 26 日在第一次到池州，便与同行专家们发现并喜欢上国润祁红旧厂房的。其感知至少有三点。

第一步，发现与认定之旅。从 2017 年 8 月 24 日第一次走进国润祁红厂，由对朴素之美的工业遗存的"活态"感悟，联想到中国 20 世纪建筑遗产的评定标准，体会着它传承至今的珍遗，更从殷天霁厂长的谈吐中多了一份感动和自信。2017 年 10 月初在池州市人民政府支持下，考察组的调研、访谈、摄影与一次次研讨不断展开。

第二步，发现与评估。2017 年 10 月初，中国文物学会 20 世纪建筑遗产委员会便组织了专家团队，并没有简单以国润祁红旧厂房入选"第二批中国 20 世纪建筑遗产项目"为目标，深度在于用此"引爆"文化池州的"城市文化工程"。一方面要从

学理上充分论证"国润祁红"的厂房建筑体现了新中国初创时是怎样的风采，这个面积与产值都不大的"茶厂"何以成为中国 20 世纪建筑工业遗产的特殊名片；另一方面，利用品质名扬天下的祁红茶，串接起中国正实施的"一带一路"发展之策，创出有社会文化"大价值"的祁红格调、情感、心态与生活方式。曾四次出任英国首相的格拉德斯通（1809–1898）有句名言："如果你发冷，茶会使你温暖；如果你发热，茶会使你凉快；如果你抑郁，茶会使你欢快；如果你激动，茶会使你平静。"

第三步，设计考察与祁红品牌传播。继 2018 年元月向池州市人民政府提出 12 条《国润祁红贵池茶厂老厂区创意设计规划要点》后，我们于 2018 年 3 月 3 日 —5 日组织全国设计大师、著名规划建筑文博专家再度考察"国润祁红"，旨在为 3 月中旬在故宫宝蕴楼召开研讨会做好准备。

为传播祁红"故事"，2018 年 4 月下旬我们再赴池州祁红，与市文广新局、规划局领导共议"国润祁红"事项，当置身于霄坑茶田，感悟到唯有绿水青山，才有生态好茶；唯有以禅入茶，才有文化立基茶禅的道之境界。这是一本试图要讲好"国润祁红"故事与品质的书。为此，需要再介绍一个事实：

据报载，2015 年 10 月 20 日下午 17 时，习近平夫妇访英期间与查尔斯王子在克劳伦斯宫一同享用著名的英式下午茶，这茶一般选用祁门红茶再加工。对中国人说来，不论是开门七件事的"柴米油盐酱醋茶"，还是文人雅士的"琴棋书画

诗酒茶"，中国文化与生活绝离不开茶，英国人喝茶以红茶居多，下午茶则是另一种文化。2015 年 10 月 20 日，在英国白金汉宫国宴上，习主席致辞中说："中国的茶叶为英国人的生活增添了诸多雅趣，英国人别具匠心地将其调制成英式红茶。中英文明交流互鉴为人类发展做出了巨大贡献。"习主席在英国传递的祁红"故事"，说明祁门红茶确有理由带给中国与世界一道靓丽的风景。

为了国润祁红旧厂房入选中国 20 世纪建筑遗产项目名录，为了理解文化池州的"茶人茶事"感人故事，《中国建筑文化遗产》编辑部专家团队至少八次造访池州贵池工厂，在念往事中，话祁红，意在为祁红故事掀开新篇。如今贵池厂区已能看到有导向标识的"国润祁红"的展示平台，说明祁门红茶的传播已走上日程。早在 2017 年初，外交部部长王毅在品"国润祁红"茶后，就评价其为"镶着金边的女王"，这是多么到位的中国茶文化的宣传语呀！为今人建构起一种更丰富的茶生活体验：走千年百年茶路、住茶农的"客房"、吃茶的餐饮、品茶的滋味、听茶的故事、讲茶的文化、享茶的禅韵等，都希望用茶带来健康和愉悦……

我特别想说的是，与其说是"国润祁红"旧厂房的精湛打动了我，倒不如说是殷厂长独有的执着与坚守感染着我。如果站在改革 40 年的"节点"上看，贵池厂留下的是匆匆的开放步伐，是"国润祁红"人不屈的发展足迹；如果站在中华人民共和国 70 年的"史实"上想，老房屋留下的亦建筑、亦工艺、亦什物的传承，就是一

组新中国工业文化的"绝照"。当我们几次派出摄影师为那弥漫着茶香的"仓库"拍照时，从那一幅幅泛红色的照片中，我们看到了祁门红茶的"颜色"，更体会到殷厂长为什么拒绝了所有开发商，坚守到"文化池州"开启建设这一天。因为池州有数十万茶农、茶工的"乡愁"，透视出全民族对中华茶文化美味的尊崇与自觉。

"国润祁红"何以能发生并创造着"奇迹"，它给世间仅仅是以茶学师、以茶悟心、以茶缘友吗？仅仅是贵池老厂房"活态"使用中透析出的历史记忆与当代启示？我以为对遗产传承与创意皆为使命的当下，它的奇迹是要在旧传承中建设新标杆，在告慰中国茶文化的同时拓展到东方文化与文化世界。

我坚信这里会出现中国乃至世界的"祁红"新品牌，因为在"一带一路"精神下，它必将成为聚拢全球三大高香茶的世界茶文化博览园。"国润祁红"的文化池州模式有它发生的逻辑，更有它迈向成功的理由。所有这些均成为我们团队着力研究、品读、传播推荐它的动力。

Jin Lei
金磊

Deputy Head and Secretary-general of the 20th Century Architectural Heritage Committee of China Cultural Relics Academy
中国文物学会 20 世纪建筑遗产委员会 副会长、秘书长

July 2018
2018 年 7 月

First Published by Tianjin University Press in 2018

This edition published by Unicorn
an imprint of Unicorn Publishing Group LLP, 2021
5 Newburgh Street
London W1F 7RG
www.unicornpublishing.org

10 9 8 7 6 5 4 3 2 1

ISBN 978-1-912690-91-6

Designed by Matthew Wilson / mexington.co.uk

Printed in the UK by Scantech

The Guorun Keemun Old Factory displayed at China's 20th Century
Architectural Heritage on Weiyuanlou Square in Quanzhou in May 2018

2018 年 5 月，在泉州威远楼广场上参展"中国 20 世纪建筑遗
产"的国润茶叶祁门红茶旧厂房。